THE STORY OF
Daniel Boone

LIQUID BOOKS

Soon he was doing all the hunting

Weekly Reader Books presents

THE STORY OF
Daniel Boone

By WILLIAM O. STEELE

Illustrated by WARREN BAUMGARTNER

ENID LAMONTE MEADOWCROFT
Supervising Editor

PUBLISHERS Grosset & Dunlap NEW YORK

For
QUINTARD AND JENIFER AND ALLERTON

Contents

Illustrations

[*ix*]

THE STORY OF
Daniel Boone

He started down the path to the woods

CHAPTER ONE

Quakers Don't Fight

THE early morning sun shone through the open door of the Boone cabin. It glinted on the pewter pitcher Elizabeth Boone was carrying to the puncheon table.

She poured the milk into wooden bowls and handed one to each of her brothers as they sat around the table. Then she set the pitcher down beside nine-year-old Daniel.

"I don't aim for you to drink it all, Dan'l," she warned.

Mary slipped into her place on the puncheon bench between Daniel and little George. She was a fair-haired girl of seven.

"I want some milk, too," Mary cried.

"There's plenty of milk," exclaimed Mrs. Boone, placing a trencher of hot ash cake on

[*3*]

the table. "Thee is lazy, Elizabeth. Thee doesn't want to fetch another pitcher of milk from the spring."

Israel, the oldest brother, pulled Elizabeth's brown braids, as he leaned over to fill Mary's bowl and then his own again.

"Elizabeth's always trying to boss me," remarked Daniel. "Just because she's a year older than me, she thinks she can tell *me* what to do."

"Elizabeth's right, Ma," grinned Samuel, who was fifteen. "Dan'l eats more than all the rest of us put together. I can't, to save me, see where the young 'un puts it."

As he spoke, Samuel piled his own trencher high with bread, fried venison collops, and thick slabs of bacon.

"Well, goodness knows, feeding the lot of you is a task," sighed Mrs. Boone as she sat down and began to help the baby, Edward, with his mush.

"Aye, Sarah, they eat a power of meal and meat," said Squire Boone from the head of the table. "But they're a fine lot. I don't believe we'd swap 'em." He smiled down the table at his wife and eight children.

[4]

Mrs. Boone laughed. "Nay, Squire, thee knows I wouldn't be without a one of them. Not even if they were the worst rogues in the world."

Her eyes rested a moment on Daniel. This was her favorite child, this blue-eyed, sandy-haired boy. Though he was good-natured and slow to anger, he was proud and independent.

Something about Daniel set him apart from the others. Perhaps it was his calm, quiet ways, and his love of being outdoors.

"Why, Ma would love us better if we *were* worthless," laughed Jonathan, who was thirteen. "Dan'l is Ma's favorite and he's the worst rogue of the lot. He's no good at weaving and not much better in the smithy. There's no use a-tall trying to make a farmer out of him. He'll always drop his hoe to run after a fox or a weasel. And as for book-learning!" Jonathan shook his head.

"That's true," Elizabeth went on severely. "He can't cipher at all. And his spelling gets worse and worse."

"Never mind," Israel consoled Daniel. "You're a heap better at shooting than most boys your age. Did you finish my ramrod?"

[5]

Israel had asked Daniel to whittle a hickory ramrod for his rifle. In return Israel had promised to let Daniel shoot the gun. Mr. Boone felt that Daniel was too young to have a rifle of his own, in spite of the fact that the boy was a good shot.

"No, I ain't," Daniel answered. "But I'll work on it this morning after breakfast, Israel."

"First, thee must fetch me a sassafras stick, Dan'l," said Mrs. Boone. "I'll make soap today because tomorrow Sarah and the baby will come for a visit." Mrs. Boone's eyes lighted at the thought of seeing her oldest child and her grandchild.

"I cut a stick yesterday, to stir the clothes with," protested Samuel.

"Aye, but thee cut me a hickory stick. It takes a sassafras stick to stir the soap and make it good," answered Mrs. Boone. "Dan'l will know where to get me a good one."

After breakfast Daniel tended to a few chores. As he fetched buckets of water from the spring to the cabin, he sniffed the pleasant smells of early summer.

He was glad he was going on this errand for

[6]

his mother. Otherwise he might have to go out to the cornfield to chop weeds, or worse yet, sit down with the hated speller.

Finally all his tasks were done. He set down the last piggin of water and ran out of the cabin. Then he picked up the axe and started down the path to the woods.

"Don't be gone all morning," Elizabeth called after him.

[7]

" 'Mulberry leaves and calico sleeves; Elizabeth Boone is hard to please,' " sang Daniel over his shoulder.

He passed his father's weaving house. From inside came the thump, thump of the loom as two of his brothers wove cloth to sell in Philadelphia fifty miles away.

A little farther from the house he could see his father's blacksmith shop. He could hear the clang of iron on the anvil as his father pounded away at a horseshoe.

In the afternoon Daniel would have to go to the blacksmith shop to help at the forge and pump the bellows. Right now these jobs were being done by Mr. Boone's apprentice, a husky twelve-year-old named Henry Miller.

Henry and Daniel were good friends. Daniel wished Henry was with him now. There was plenty they could do together this fine morning.

A moment later Daniel was in the woods.

The June morning was warm, but here under the trees the air was sweet and cool. He loved the woods. There wasn't a place he'd rather be than in the woods.

[8]

Only he did wish he had a rifle.

He came to a clearing and surprised a rab·bit. He stopped to watch a woodpecker search·ing in the cracks of the tree bark for insects.

He raised an imaginary rifle and said aloud, "Bang! I shot the biggest turkey!"

The woodpecker looked around at him and Daniel laughed. "I know you're a wood-pecker," he said to the bird and went on his way.

Soon he reached a place where sassafras trees grew thickly. He picked out a small tree and began to chop. He knew how to handle an axe and in a few strokes the tree fell.

"Hey, there!" called a voice. "What do you think you're doing?"

Daniel looked up. A boy he had never seen before stood glaring at him. "I'm cutting down a tree," Daniel answered evenly. He be-gan to trim the limbs from the fallen trunk.

"Here, stop that! Don't you know better than to cut down folks' trees?" the strange boy asked.

Daniel never looked up, as he replied, "Not when they're my folks' trees."

[9]

"Your folks! This here land belongs to my pa!" the boy screamed at Daniel.

Daniel flipped his hatchet down. The blade stuck in the trunk and the handle quivered. He turned toward the stranger.

"Now this here is my pa's land," he said reasonably. "His name is Squire Boone and his land comes right up to that beech tree there with the blaze on it."

"And I reckon he owns half of Pennsylvania," the other boy sneered.

"No, he don't," answered Daniel goodnaturedly. "But he owns this tree, and I aim to take it home."

He put out his hand for his hatchet.

The new boy grabbed his arm. "Don't you touch that hatchet!" he cried angrily. "This is my pa's land, and if you cut down a tree you must pay for it."

"Pay for it?" Daniel exclaimed.

He looked the stranger up and down. The boy was wearing town-bought clothes, not rough homespun shirt and breeches as Daniel was. He was not taller than Daniel, but he was heavier.

Daniel reached for the hatchet again. The other boy's fist shot out and hit him squarely on the cheek. Daniel staggered backward a step. His face hurt.

He stood up. The stranger raised both fists. "Want another blow just like that?" he asked. "Come on."

Daniel took a step forward. Suddenly he kicked the other boy's shin. The boy hopped on one foot, holding his other leg.

[*11*]

Daniel punched him in the nose. Blood spurted out. The stranger turned and ran.

"There," said Daniel, "that'll teach you not to fight."

He picked up his axe and finished trimming the limbs from the tree. Then he shouldered the trunk and started home.

On the way back to the cabin he stopped to feel the knot on the side of his face. What a lump!

When he reached home, his father and his

brothers stood in the clearing behind the cabin, talking to Mrs. Boone. She was making a fire under a big kettle for the soap.

"Here's the sassafras stick, Ma," Daniel called cheerfully.

"I knew thee would find a good one," answered his mother, as she fed the fire with pieces of dry wood.

His brother Israel laughed "He's had to fight for it." He pointed at Daniel's cheek.

"Dan'l, thee has been fighting!" exclaimed Mrs. Boone. "Thee knows that Quakers do not fight."

"It wasn't me that started it," Daniel said, and he told what had happened.

"That would be Mr. Wayne's boy. Mr. Wayne just bought the land next to ours," said Daniel's father, rubbing his chin. "I've heard they were bad neighbors."

"Now see, Dan'l," said Mrs. Boone. "Thee was hasty. Thee's made an enemy of a neighbor. Shame!"

The older boys laughed. "Our Dan'l did right," they told their mother. "He's a good fighter when he has to be."

Mr. Boone shook his head. "It's getting too

[*13*]

crowded here in Oley Township," he said. "Neighbors ought not to be so close that you can quarrel with them. We're going to have to move to some place where we can have a little more land around us."

Daniel's heart leaped for joy.

"Where can we go, Pa?" he asked eagerly. "Into the wilderness?" He would like to move right into the very middle of the wilderness where there would be no neighbors at all.

"The wilderness!" scoffed Samuel. "It would be better for you if you moved into a schoolroom. Go get a hoe and come help me weed the corn."

Sadly Daniel moved off to get his hoe. Weeding was better than ciphering. But he *did* wish they could move into the wilderness.

CHAPTER TWO

The Round Bird

DANIEL stood in the clearing outside his father's blacksmith shop, gazing at the sky.

A moment before the October sun had been shining brightly, but now the sky was darkened by a flock of passenger pigeons. The birds flew low overhead, filling the sky as far as Daniel could see. He could hardly believe there were so many birds in the world.

His neck began to hurt, but still he kept his head bent back to watch the pigeons.

A voice spoke close behind him, "What're you doing, young 'un?"

Daniel jumped. The noise of the flying birds had kept him from hearing anyone approach. He turned quickly to see a lanky man in buckskins.

[*15*]

"Howdy, Mr. Mason," he said with a grin.

Pete Mason was a hunter. In between his hunting trips into the wilderness he lived on his brother's farm in Oley Township.

Daniel liked the friendly old hunter. He was never too busy to tell wonderful tales of the game he had killed and the places he had been.

"I'm counting to see how many pigeons are in this bunch going over," Daniel told the hunter.

"Tarnation, Dan'l," drawled Mr. Mason, "this flock ain't no size a-tall. Why, out in the woods, I've seen flocks so big—the pigeons were so thick in the air, a feller couldn't breathe. I've had to go down into caves many a time to get a decent breath of air."

Daniel laughed, but the hunter's wrinkled face stayed solemn. Then he gave Daniel a wink and walked inside the smithy. He placed his rifle against the wall by the wide-open door.

Daniel followed him. He could see pigeons some other time. Pete Mason wasn't around the settlement often. Daniel didn't want to miss a word the hunter had to say.

"Howdy, Squire. Howdy, Henry," called Mr. Mason over the clang of the hammer. "You folks are mighty busy."

"We got to get through with Mr. Wayne's wagon wheel. He thinks he's a mighty important man and he needs his wagon right away," Mr. Boone said with a twinkle in his eye.

"I never heard of him," remarked Mr. Mason.

"You will if you stay around long enough, Pete," Mr. Boone told him as he laid down his hammer. "He owns a right smart heap of land hereabouts. You've been gone almost a year, ain't you? The Waynes moved in last spring while you were off hunting."

"Where did you go this time, Mr. Mason?" asked Henry Miller.

"Oh, over across the mountains and round about," replied Mr. Mason.

"Did you shoot any buffalo?" asked Daniel.

"I did, Dan'l."

"Any big ones?"

"Well, one of them buffaloes I shot was right good sized." Mr. Mason looked down into the blue eyes of Daniel. "I shot one buffalo that was so big I had to look three times to see all of him."

Mr. Boone and the boys broke into laughter. Mr. Boone took off his deerskin apron.

"I have to go up to the weaving house," he said. "Pete, I hope you stay around the settlement a spell. Don't go off again so soon."

He started outside, but when he reached the doorway he looked around. "Put that wheel on the wagon, so it'll be ready for Mr. Wayne, Henry," he commanded. "Get Dan'l to help you."

"All right, sir," answered Henry. He turned back to the hunter. "Mr. Mason, tell us some more stories."

Mr. Mason leaned against the anvil and began to tell the boys about his travels. The fire in the forge died down. Mr. Wayne's horses stamped their feet impatiently outside.

Henry and Daniel had forgotten the wagon wheel. With the old hunter they roamed the wide meadows and the tall forests of the wilderness. Daniel could almost see the bear and buffalo and deer, as he listened to Mr. Mason tell one tale after another.

Suddenly a man's voice bellowed outside the smithy.

Henry jumped a foot. "That's Mr. Wayne," he muttered. "We're in for it, Dan'l."

"Why in thunder isn't my wagon ready?" Mr. Wayne roared as he strode angrily into the blacksmith shop. "Where's Mr. Boone? This is a fine way to run a smithy! My wagon was promised for noon, and it's noon now!"

"I'm sorry, sir," answered Henry. "Mr. Boone ain't here. We'll have your wheel on in a moment, sir. Come on, Dan'l."

Henry began to roll the wheel outside. Daniel followed him. As he passed Mr. Wayne, he glanced up into his face. Mr. Wayne had the hardest, meanest-looking eyes he had ever seen.

"You tell Boone I won't pay. My wagon wasn't ready like he promised. I tell you I won't pay good money for poor work," Mr. Wayne shouted.

He followed the boys outside. "Get busy, you no-good, worthless imps! And be quick about it. I've been kept waiting long enough."

In a short time the two boys had the wheel on the wagon and the horses hitched. Mr. Wayne, still grumbling, climbed hastily into the wagon. Picking up his whip, he lashed the horses and drove off in a cloud of dust.

Mr. Mason came out of the smithy with his rifle over his shoulder. "Boys, that's one reason I live in the wilderness," he announced. "Plenty of room and no one to talk sassy. Where I go, the creatures speak decent to you."

Mr. Mason moved off. Daniel admired the silent way the hunter walked in his buckskin moccasins.

[22]

But Henry was not thinking about the hunter. "Your pa will be mad when he finds out Mr. Wayne wouldn't pay," he said gloomily.

"Old goat!" exclaimed Daniel. "He needn't have gone home in such an all-fired hurry. I'd like to—"

Suddenly he leaned over to the other boy and said, "Listen, Henry, I'll tell you what we'll do tonight . . ." He whispered a few more words.

Henry's eyes shone. "We'll do it!" he exclaimed. "I'll meet you by Wayne's barn as soon as it's dark."

The stars were out when Daniel and Henry met behind the Wayne barn. The air was crisp and a few dry leaves rattled beneath the boys' feet as they crept around to the front of the barn.

A light shone through the window of the Waynes' cabin. Daniel could see Mr. Wayne standing in front of the fire. But the cabin and barn were separated by a wide clearing. The candlelight from the window did not reach the boys as they slipped into the big barn.

[23]

One of the doors had been left open. The cows were munching hay in their stalls. A horse snorted and bumped about.

"Now be real quiet," Henry whispered. "The wagon's back yonder, I reckon."

Daniel stepped forward cautiously. All at once his foot rolled on something under the hay. He flung out his arms and knocked Henry against one of the horse stalls. Henry's head bumped heavily on the boards. He groaned aloud. The horse neighed loudly.

"Quick, hide over here," Daniel muttered. "They'll be out to see what made that rumpus, for sure."

Swiftly they crawled into the hay beside the cattle stalls. With thumping hearts they waited for some sign of life from the Wayne house. But none came.

Henry rubbed his head. "I got a knot on my head," he said softly.

"Never mind," answered Daniel. "Let's get that wagon wheel and get out of here."

They groped their way to the wagon. Henry felt for the linch pin that held the wheel. A few moments later they were quietly rolling

[24]

the big wagon wheel out of the Wayne barn.

The two boys came out into the clearing. It was quite dark, and the wheel was heavy and hard to manage.

They shoved and pushed. Suddenly the Waynes' door flew open. A light streamed out over the clearing. Mr. Wayne came out into the yard, holding a lantern high.

Daniel and Henry froze in their tracks. They were too startled to move. The light flickered around them, this way and that. Once

Mr. Wayne held the lantern still and slanted it at some bushes. But finally he lowered the light.

"I could have sworn I heard somebody out there," he said to someone in the house, as he closed the door.

"That was close," whispered Henry.

"It sure was," Daniel replied. "He had his gun in his other hand and might have shot us. Come on, let's get away from here."

They pushed the wheel up the hill. At last they came out on the road. Now the way was easier. The boys rolled the big wheel ahead of them like a hoop.

"There," Daniel pointed. "That big oak will do, Henry. We've got to hurry."

Daniel tied one end of a rope to the wheel. Then he climbed the tree, holding the other end. Henry waited below. There was a muffled cry, and much shaking of dry leaves.

"What's the matter?" cried Henry. "Are you falling?"

"I stepped on an owl," answered Daniel. "Catch this end."

He threw down the other end of the rope,

"Wait! Wait!" cried Daniel. "It's stuck!"

which he had crossed over a limb. Henry began to pull with all his strength. Slowly the wheel rose in the air, bumping against the tree. Daniel climbed down and helped Henry pull.

"Wait! Wait!" cried Daniel. "It's stuck!"

"Get it loose before I drop it," gasped Henry.

Finally the wheel was firmly wedged in a crotch of the tree. Daniel untied the rope and came down.

"Mr. Wayne's going to be surprised in the morning," he told Henry.

And they laughed together, as they ran through the dark toward their homes.

The next morning Daniel and Henry were both at the blacksmith shop early. But Mr. Boone was there before them. And so was Pete Mason.

"Howdy, boys," said Pete as they came in.

"Dan'l, I was just telling your pa about some birds I saw when I was out on my last hunting trip. Round birds they was. Round as a wheel and they didn't have no legs. When you shot 'em, they just flopped to the ground and rolled away."

[28]

Something about the way Mr. Mason talked made both boys look at him suspiciously. Mr. Boone laughed at his tale.

"I thought I saw one of them birds setting in that big oak tree by the trace as I come along this morning," Mr. Mason went on. "Leastways I thought it was a round bird. Mr. Wayne was there and he seemed to think it was a wagon wheel."

"A wagon wheel!" exclaimed Mr. Boone. He turned toward his son. "All right, Dan'l. You've been up to mischief again, I know. Tell me the truth about it or I'll take a hickory switch to your legs."

"Pa," said Daniel. "Mr. Wayne wouldn't pay for fixing his wheel yesterday, because he had to wait while me and Henry put it on. He's the meanest man in Pennsylvania. He's always doing hateful things. So last night me and Henry went over to his barn and took that wagon wheel off. We hauled it up in that big oak tree."

Mr. Boone looked serious. "I know the kind of man Wayne is," he said. "But you did wrong, boys, not to put the wheel on when I told you to do it yesterday."

[29]

Daniel remained quiet. It was worth a whipping just to have Mr. Wayne put out about his wheel.

"Dan'l," said his father slowly. "I guess it was your idea to put the wheel in the tree. And if I was your mother, I'd whip you good. But I ain't, so . . ."

Mr. Boone stopped speaking and laughed. He put his hand on Daniel's shoulder.

"It kind of makes me feel good to know you evened things up with old Wayne," he said, giving the boy a friendly little shake. "But the *next* time I hear about a round bird in a tree, I'll . . . oh, go on, Dan'l, and bring me in some charcoal. It's time we got to work."

Daniel grinned and looked at Henry. Then he ran to get the charcoal for his father.

CHAPTER THREE

The Panther

THE next summer Daniel's father bought a tract of land some distance from the Boones' home. Grazing was good on this land, and Mr. Boone planned to drive his cattle there. The cows would feed well all summer and grow sleek and fat.

"We'll build a cabin there," Mr. Boone told his sons. "Your ma can stay there till the weather gets cold. And one of you boys will have to go with her to watch the cows and help her milk and churn."

He looked at Daniel. "You're the one to go, I reckon. I'll never make a farmer out of you, Dan'l. You might as well be out in the woods with the cows."

Daniel was delighted.

[31]

"I reckon I'll need a rifle," he told his father.

"Your mother will have my old musket," answered Mr. Boone. "But I don't want you to touch it, do you hear? Ten is still too young to be turned loose with a rifle."

Daniel sighed. He often shot his brothers' rifles. He thought he was pretty good at it, too.

But life at the grazing farm was fun for Daniel even without a rifle. He drove the cows out to pasture in the morning. All day he stayed in

the woods and fields, keeping an eye on the cows. At dusk he brought them home.

The work was easy. Daniel missed his brothers and Henry Miller at first. But he had plenty of time to do the things he liked to do—to watch the birds, to learn the tracks made by different animals, and to find the places which they had chosen for their homes.

He studied the trees, too, and the skies and the wind. Before long he decided that he would rather be in the woods than anywhere else in the world. He would have been perfectly happy—if only he had a rifle.

Every week Mr. Boone or one of the older boys rode out to the grazing farm to bring food and other necessities to Daniel and his mother, and to take the butter back home to be sold.

One June evening during the summer Daniel was twelve years old, Mr. Boone arrived on horseback to get the butter.

Daniel heard the horse and ran from the cabin to meet his father.

"Here's the salt and meal, Sarah," said Mr. Boone, getting down from his horse and beginning to unload his saddlebags. "And here

[33]

is a bundle of quilt scraps Elizabeth sent you, and a new needle."

He rummaged through the bags again. "That's all," he announced. "Though it did seem I had something for Dan'l."

"Pa," said Daniel, "why have you got two rifles?"

"Why, I've heard tell there's a two-headed turkey in these woods. I aim to be ready to shoot it," answered Mr. Boone with a twinkle in his eye. Then he went on. "Here, Dan'l, here's the rifle you've been craving. And here's a powder horn Israel give you. Your mother can make you a shot pouch."

With trembling hands Daniel took the gun and the hollowed-out cow's horn. A rifle! His very own! He was a hunter at last.

"Thank you, Pa," he stammered finally. "I'll shoot so many deer, you'll never lack for meat. I'll get enough hides to pay for the gun this fall."

"We'll see," laughed Mr. Boone. He went into the cabin, leaving Daniel fingering his gun in delight.

In spite of his promises, Daniel had his gun

[34]

for a whole week and only shot a few rabbits.

One morning he planned to go to a place where he might find a deer. But at breakfast his mother told him that one of their cows had strayed in the night.

"Thee must bring in the cow, Dan'l, before thee goes hunting," she said.

"All right, Ma," he answered, swallowing the last of his buttered ash bread.

Then he took his rifle, his powder horn, and

his shot bag, and ran from the cabin. Soon he was out in the woods hunting the cow.

"Hoo-ey, cow. Hoo-eeeee," called Daniel. "Where is that fool cow?

"Hoooo, bossy," he called once more.

He stopped to listen for the jingle of the bell that each of the Boone cows wore around its neck. He heard nothing but the rattle of a kingfisher from the near-by creek.

Wiping the sweat from his forehead, Daniel looked out through the trees. It was a hot June day, but here under these great trees the air was cool.

"I'll look over toward the creek," he said to himself, "and then I'll swing back toward the ridge."

He struck off through the woods and came out at a bend in the creek. Dropping to his knees to drink, he noticed the water at the edge of the creek was reddish.

What was that red color?

It was blood! He was on his feet in an instant. He'd bet a pretty it was the cow's blood. Wading upstream, he found the remains of the missing cow. He searched the bank of the

creek, looking at the tracks in the mud.
"It's as plain as daylight," he said aloud.
"The cow came here to drink and a painter
killed her. Let's see, now. The big cat's tracks

go off this way. I believe I'll just follow that
painter and twist his tail. I'll let Mr. Painter
know he'd best eat somebody else's cows."

He followed the panther tracks easily up
the creek for a distance. Then he lost the trail
where a rock stuck out into the water.

Daniel stopped. "Let's see. Now if I was a painter, I'd jump to that rock so my footprints wouldn't show," he said to himself.

He crawled up on the rock. "Now, where would I go?"

There was a series of rocks, large and small, like steppingstones going up the bank. Daniel went to the last one. "Now, if I was still a painter, I'd jump to that fallen log and then to the ground."

Daniel jumped. Just beyond the log, he found the panther's footprints again. He trailed the cat off toward a low ridge.

It was at the foot of the tangled, rocky slope that he finally stopped. He was getting a little uneasy. Although he had a gun and could use it, still panthers were ferocious critters. And they had more sense than an animal ought to have, Daniel thought.

There was something about the shape of the rocks before him that made Daniel think there might be a den behind them.

He looked. Then he got away fast. There was no doubt in his mind that he had found the panther's den.

[38]

He climbed a tree where he could see the entrance clearly. He checked the powder in the pan of his gun to make sure he had not knocked it out as he climbed the tree.

Carefully he placed the rifle in a fork of the tree and sat to wait for the panther. It was hot in the tree. The morning sun rose higher until it was right overhead. Then it began to go down and Daniel began to nod.

"I reckon that painter is scared to death of me," he said to himself. "It's probably hiding in that calico bush down there, shaking from head to foot."

He looked sleepily at the bush. Suddenly he was wide awake. A slow chill crept over him. A moment ago just the bush had been there. Now a flat tawny head stuck out of the branches. Two bright yellow eyes looked all about.

The panther opened its huge mouth and snarled softly. Daniel could see its great white teeth gleaming. He shivered a little.

The panther came out of the bushes, padding softly on its big paws. The muscles under its yellow fur rippled across its shoulders. It

[39]

Quickly Daniel squeezed the trigger

was the biggest panther Daniel had ever seen.

The panther started toward its den, then stopped and sniffed the ground where Daniel had walked.

Quickly Daniel sighted behind the big cat's left shoulder and squeezed the trigger.

The gun went off. The panther gave a yowling scream, turning toward Daniel's tree. It leaped forward and fell dead at the base of the tree.

Daniel sat a minute on his branch, looking down at the beast. Suddenly he grinned.

"We did it," he said, and patted his gun.

Daniel was soon a fine shot. He had the keen eye and the calm, patient disposition of the natural-born hunter.

In a year or so he was doing all the hunting for the Boones. Mr. Boone bragged about his son's skill, and Mrs. Boone was proud that her table was always amply provided with meat.

Daniel hunted in the colder months and helped his mother with the cows in summer. The years went by. Daniel grew taller and leaner and always more skillful with his rifle.

Oley Township grew too, and settlers came

crowding into the woods. Sometimes it was hard to find game. Daniel had to travel farther and farther into the woods to shoot a deer.

One day Mr. Boone came for the noon meal and spoke to Daniel.

"Son," he teased, "we've had squirrel stew three days running. I reckon the deer have heard about you and your rifle. They've took off for Injun country, where they'll be safe."

"It ain't me they're running from," Daniel answered. "It's all these folks. I ain't seen a bear or deer in ten miles of this cabin since all these fields were cleared around us. And more people keep coming all the time. Last week I was looking for a deer. I heard something in the bushes and I thought sure it was a deer. But it was three other fellers out hunting too. No wonder there ain't any game."

Mr. Boone looked around the table at his family. "You all heard what Dan'l said?" he asked. "Well, things will be different soon."

"How come, Pa?" asked Jonathan.

"I've sold the farm," announced Mr. Boone. "We're moving to Caroliny."

"Yippee!" shouted Daniel.

[42]

"Yippee!" echoed his little brother, Squire.

The other brothers and sisters looked pleased. But tears came into Mrs. Boone's eyes at the thought of leaving her older married children and her comfortable farm to go into the wilderness.

It took many weeks for the Boones to sell off their possessions and get ready to move. But one day in April they loaded their pack horses with powder and lead, extra clothes, blankets, and cooking pots. And off they started on their long journey to North Carolina.

Adventures aplenty lay before them in that wilderness.

CHAPTER FOUR

The Wilderness

N OW you be careful with that axe," Daniel
warned his young brother, Squire.

Squire was eight now, ten years younger
than Daniel.

"I reckon I'm pretty handy with an axe," re-
torted Squire. "Don't you be telling me what
to do all the time."

Daniel laughed. "You're a real Boone,
Squire," he remarked. "None of us like to have
folks telling us what to do and how to do it."

Squire went on chopping limbs from the
tree the two brothers had just felled.

The Boones were building a cabin on their
new home place in North Carolina. All the
children were working hard to get the cabin
finished. Mrs. Boone was anxious to have a
good cabin built before winter.

Daniel had left the others looking for a tree just the right size to support the rafters for the roof. With Squire he had come quite a distance through the woods till he found a tree that just suited him. It was a fine straight poplar tree.

After a few minutes of chopping, Squire straightened up. "Whee! My back's tired," he complained.

"Come on," Daniel teased. "That's no way for a handy man with an axe to do. We got to get our cabin finished quick. Ma will skin us alive if it turns cold before we get the cabin done."

"You ain't worried about what Ma will do," said Squire. "You just want to get through with the cabin so you can go hunting."

"It's good hunting weather all right," said Daniel with a grin. There was a sound of rustling leaves and Daniel turned quickly.

A man in buckskins was walking through the woods toward them, swinging a rifle.

"Howdy," called the stranger. "You folks settling in?"

"Aye," answered Daniel. "We're getting us a cabin up. Be you living near by?"

"My name's Burk Williams," said the stranger. "I live about six miles south of here. I heard tell there was a new family on the Yadkin River, so I come to see if it was true. Welcome to the colony of North Carolina."

"We're true enough," laughed Daniel. "Our name's Boone. I'm Dan'l and this here chap is Squire. We come from Pennsylvania. Is the hunting pretty good around here?"

"I shot two bucks from my front door this

morning," answered Mr. Williams. "This is fine country. Deer and bear just knock on the door and beg you to shoot them."

"Dan'l," called Mr. Boone. "Where be ye?" In a minute he came in sight through the trees, muttering as he came. "You had no call to go so far from the cabin. I've passed twenty trees already that would do good enough. The trouble with you is, you can't go a little piece out in the woods. You got to go just a little farther and a little farther—" He broke off when he saw Mr. Williams.

Daniel introduced his father to their new neighbor.

Mr. Boone told Mr. Williams how much land he wanted to buy. He told how the Boone family had left Pennsylvania to come south when Daniel was sixteen. For some time they had traveled and looked for a place where the land was rich, the neighbors not too close, and game plentiful.

"Well, you've found it here in the Yadkin Valley," stated Mr. Williams. "But if it's game you want, you ought to go west."

He pointed through the trees to a line of

mountains in the west. "That's the Blue Ridge," he went on, "and it's as full of bear and deer as a gourd is of seeds."

After a little more talk, Mr. Williams left. Squire and Mr. Boone waved after him, but Daniel didn't even see him go. He was looking toward the west, toward the misty blue mountains that were full of game.

"I got to go there," he told himself softly. Then he called, "Hurry up, Squire! We got to get back and help the others finish this cabin."

Soon the cabin was finished and the Boones were settled. Then Daniel was free to hunt whenever he wanted to. And he began to explore the country beyond the Yadkin Valley. He explored farther and farther west, toward the Blue Ridge Mountains. And the farther away he went, the better was the hunting. Time after time he returned to the cabin with his pack horse loaded with meat and deer hides and bearskins.

One day he went to Salisbury, which was the nearest town, to trade his furs and deer hides for powder and lead.

Salisbury wasn't much of a town. There

were only a few stores and log cabins, a jail, and a courthouse.

"Whoa there, Red!" Daniel called to his pack horse.

He stopped in front of Conners' Trading Post. Loosening the strap that held the skins on the horse's back, he eased the bundle onto his shoulder. As soon as he was inside the store, he dropped the skins onto a puncheon table.

"Why, it's Dan'l Boone," said Mr. Conners, coming toward him.

"Howdy, sir," answered Daniel.

While the trader counted the hides, Daniel looked around the store. There were bolts of calico, ribbons, mirrors, and needles for the women folks.

[50]

Tables held knives, guns, flints, and tomahawks for the men. Around the walls sat barrels of brown sugar and powder. In one corner,
bars of lead were stacked in neat piles.

Real money was as scarce as frog hair in the
back country of North Carolina. Deerskins
took the place of silver coins.

Daniel moved over to the table of tomahawks. He picked up one to judge its balance
and weight. He went back to the storekeeper.

"I want this here hatchet," he said. "And
two bars of lead. And this wallet full of the
best powder you've got."

"All right," answered Mr. Conners. He
looked at Daniel's skins closely. "Where did
you get them, Dan'l?"

"Over around the Blue Ridge Mountains,
sir," replied Daniel. "Fine hunting over
there."

"Well, these are prime skins all right, but
you'd better watch out," Mr. Conners warned
him. "There's hostile Injuns over there hunting for your scalp. You'd better stick closer to
home."

"I reckon I'll make out. I've taken care of

myself for twenty years. I can do it a while longer," boasted Daniel as he left with his purchases.

Daniel acted as if he were used to dealing with Indians on the warpath. But it wasn't true. He had known only friendly Indians in Pennsylvania. The Quakers had always treated the red men fairly and the Indians did not trouble the settlers there.

But hostile Indians! Indians after scalps!

Daniel decided he would have to keep a sharp eye out for them. He would not give up his exploring nor his good hunting, though.

A few days later he was ready to leave on another trip. His younger brothers and sisters were gathered around him as he loaded his pack horse with his bearskin blanket, his powder and lead, a bag of meal, a small bag of salt, and a little jerked meat to provision him till he shot a deer.

He also took an extra rifle and a few simple blacksmith tools to repair his rifle with in case it should break. With his axe and his knife and the rifle he carried on his shoulder, he was ready to set out.

"Do you reckon you'll get a buffalo this trip?" asked George.

"If you get one, bring me one of the horns," begged Squire.

Squire thought ten years old was plenty old enough to go on a hunting trip. He hated to stay at home with George and Edward, helping Mr. Boone and doing farm tasks.

"Bring me something too," begged Hannah, the youngest.

"I'll bring home a heap of skins," Daniel promised them. "Then we'll take them to the store and trade them for barley sugar."

Mrs. Boone came out just then and kissed Daniel good-by. He walked off toward the west leading his horse and waving to his brothers and sisters as long as he could see them.

A week later he had as many skins as his horse could carry. But he was not ready to return home. He wanted to do some exploring. He wanted to climb the mountains and see what lay beyond.

One morning he hid his skins in a hollow tree. Then he hobbled his horse and started up the mountain. He pushed through tangled

He saw the Indians much more plainly now

bushes and climbed around huge boulders.

At last he reached the top and stood gazing about. Other mountains stretched before him to the west as far as he could see.

He scanned the countryside eastward toward the Yadkin. Suddenly he gave a start, then dropped flat to the cliff's edge.

He had seen a file of Indians winding along a valley. Squirming over behind a rock, he peered around one side of it.

The Indians were coming from the east and heading toward him. He watched them cross a creek. Now Daniel could see they were making their way toward the place where he had left his pack horse. He could not afford to lose his horse. He would have to reach the animal before the Indians did.

Quickly he backed away from the cliff's edge. Then he stood up and ran headlong down the slope, sliding around the rocks, flying through the trees.

About halfway down he stopped in a cleared place where he could see the valley below.

He saw the Indians much more plainly now. There were twenty of them. They were in war paint and carried rifles as well as bows and arrows.

One hasty glance and Daniel was off again. When he neared the foot of the mountain, he slowed down and moved more quietly. At last he reached the canebrake where he had hobbled his horse.

He ran to the animal and took the hobbles from its feet. Taking hold of the lead thong, he pulled the horse after him into the bushes.

Then he went back and sprinkled some dead leaves over his own footprints and those of his horse. He could not hide all the marks, but he hoped the others would not be seen. Returning to his horse, he crouched in the bushes and checked his rifle.

His heart pounded as he waited for the Indians. Closer and closer they came. At last he could see them plainly.

One of the Indians was singing. The others laughed and talked. Daniel could not understand a word they said.

Each one wore moccasins and a strip of deerskin that passed between his legs and was looped over a belt in front and back. Each

[56]

brave had different designs in red and black painted on his body and face.

"They're on the warpath. That's sure," Daniel thought. "And that's a white man's medal around the leader's neck. Indians don't have trinkets like that."

He peered at the leader more closely. "That gun he's got looks like the French gun I saw once in Salisbury. Why, all of them have

French guns," he said to himself. "I wonder where they got them."

Then he saw the two scalps tied to the leader's belt. Several of the other Indians had scalps too.

Instantly he felt sick. The Indians had come from the direction of his home. Could some of those bloody scalps belong to *his* folks? He bit his lip to keep from crying out.

Just as the last Indian in the column was about to pass, he stopped. Dropping to his knee, he examined the ground. His eyes darted this way and that. He rose and moved close to Daniel's hiding place.

Daniel slowly raised his gun. If the brave discovered him, Daniel meant to make sure it was the last thing that Indian ever did.

But with a last look around the red man grunted and trotted off to catch up with the others. Daniel breathed a sigh of relief. He waited a few more minutes to make sure the way was safe. Packing his deerskins on his horse, he headed east for the Yadkin country as fast as he could go.

He had to find out if his family was safe.

CHAPTER FIVE

Daniel Hears of Kentuck

THREE days later Daniel reached his home. Smoke was coming from the chimney. Some of his folks were safe anyway!

Daniel ran into the cabin, crying, "Ma! Pa!"

He tripped over a three-legged stool and fell against his brother George. With a clatter and a loud yell from George, both brothers sprawled on the floor. The others stood around laughing as the young men tried to untangle themselves.

"Dan'l, what in tarnation is the matter with you?" asked George.

Daniel managed to sit up, pushing the stool away. He grinned up at the family. "Be you all safe?" he asked. "I reckoned the Injuns had you."

Mr. Boone shook his head. "Nay, we're all safe. The Shawnees made a raid a few days ago. But it was farther down on the Yadkin. They killed a heap of folks."

"I saw them Injuns," said Daniel. He told what he had seen as he hid in the bushes. "They had French guns, it looked like," he finished.

Mr. Boone spoke angrily. "The French are coming down from Canada and are trying to start a war with the English. That's the talk in Salisbury. The French give the Shawnees guns and powder and lead so they can raid us."

"Well, why don't they make war on the English soldiers?" asked Mrs. Boone indignantly. "Why do they come here and burn our homes and kill us?"

"We're English too," spoke Mr. Boone. "We live in the English colony of North Caroliny."

"That's right," Daniel nodded. "In Salisbury, I heard a lawyer named Richard Henderson say the colonies will have to help if England and France go to war."

Mrs. Boone looked sad. "If folks acted decent, this wouldn't happen. There was never any scalping in Pennsylvania. We Quakers treated the Indians right and they treated us the same way. We should have stayed there."

"Well, the people of North Caroliny ain't done nothing to the Shawnees. It's the French that's sent them against us," Mr. Boone said. "But I don't think these raids will last."

Mrs. Boone turned to her son. "Dan'l, why does thee want to go up in them mountains anyway?"

"I'd like to cross the mountains," Daniel answered. "I'd like to see what the country's like over there. To look around and do some hunting."

"That's a foolish notion," said Mrs. Boone. "What's wrong with the country on this side of the mountains? Thee ought to settle down and learn the blacksmith trade. Thee'll not find trouble any easier beyond the mountains than here at home, Dan'l."

Daniel smiled at his mother. "There's a heap of country over there," he told her. "With a little room, me and trouble ain't so likely to run into each other."

In the days that followed Daniel thought

often of the Blue Ridge. But he did not go back to the mountains right away.

Many years earlier, a war had started between the British and French nations that was almost world wide. That part of the war which was fought on the American continent has been called the French and Indian War.

France wanted the country between the Mississippi River and the Allegheny Mountains for her own because of the rich fur trade. The English wanted it also.

The French had built a series of forts in important points to the west of the American colonies. From these forts the French had gone out among the various Indian tribes to trade. They had persuaded many Indians to side with them against the British.

In 1755 General Edward Braddock was sent to the American colonies as commander in chief of the British forces in North America.

He had orders to capture Fort Duquesne. This was a French fort at the meeting of the Allegheny and Monongahela Rivers in western Pennsylvania.

One spring day in 1755, Daniel and Squire

were in Salisbury. They had been trading for salt, which the Boones badly needed.

"Looky yonder, Dan'l," Squire said, tugging at his brother's sleeve. "Let's go see what that man is saying."

A handful of people stood in the muddy street listening to a tall man in a soldier's uniform. As they approached, the Boone brothers could hear him speak.

"I'm Major Dodds and I'm an officer in the British Regular Army," the man announced. "I'm here to get volunteers to help General Braddock fight the French and Indians."

"What kind of volunteers be ye wanting?" asked a man in dirty buckskins who stood beside Daniel.

"I need scouts, hunters, anybody that's not afraid of a fight," the major replied.

As Daniel listened, he said to himself, "I'm twenty-one and I know the woods as well as the next fellow. Better than some. I believe I'll just volunteer."

So Daniel Boone joined the militia and was sent with other men from North Carolina to Pennsylvania.

[63]

"I believe I'll just volunteer," Daniel said

It took time to gather food and supplies for General Braddock's army. While he waited for the army to start for Fort Duquesne, Daniel had nothing to do but to talk to the other men who had enlisted as scouts and wagon drivers.

One night Daniel sat by a campfire in a woods clearing, talking to one of his companions about the British soldiers. Daniel had never seen such soldiers as the British. Dressed in scarlet coats and black hats, these troops marched smartly along the country roads or drilled in a field without once getting out of step. They marched and turned and turned again, as one man.

"Them red coats the British wear are sure bright," Daniel said admiringly.

"They're too bright," answered the other man, whose name was John Finley. "They'll make good marks for Injuns to shoot at."

"Maybe the Injuns won't shoot," said Daniel. "Maybe there won't be any fighting."

Daniel hoped there wouldn't be. He could never get over his Quaker training. He wasn't afraid. He always fought when he had to. Still he felt that killing was a terrible thing.

[65]

"Oh, there'll be fighting all right," John Finley remarked. He pushed with his foot at one of the burning logs of the fire.

"And when the fighting starts, it'll be a sad day for General Braddock's fine army."

"Do you think the French and the Injuns will win?" asked Daniel in astonishment. How could the French and Indians beat this big fine-looking army?

Mr. Finley nodded. "Braddock's army is long on looks, but short on sense. They reckon the Injuns are going to line up in rows and march to meet them in a nice open field, like regular soldiers."

He looked disgusted. "Even Colonel Washington thinks General Braddock will get beat. I heard tell the other day that he tried to persuade General Braddock not to fight in formation. The soldiers ought to take off them red coats and learn to fight from behind trees and rocks, the way the Injuns and the colonists do."

"Who's Colonel Washington?" asked Daniel curiously.

"Colonel George Washington," answered

Finley. "He's a surveyor from Virginia. He's a pretty good Injun fighter and he's got plenty of horse sense."

Daniel laughed. When Mr. Finley said horse sense, he drew his long face down and looked like a very solemn horse himself.

"You can laugh if you like," said Mr. Finley with a grin. "But it takes a smart man to fight Injuns."

"I wouldn't know." Daniel shook his head. "I never done any fighting."

"Well, I've done plenty," said Mr. Finley. "Once I even fought alongside red men when they was warring with another Injun tribe."

"Where was that?" asked Daniel.

"Oh, over beyond the mountains . . ." began Finley.

Daniel looked up, startled. "Beyond the mountains?" he inquired. "What mountains? The Carolina mountains?"

"I reckon so," Finley went on. "These same mountains that start here in Pennsylvania and run south near about to the sea, I reckon. They're pesky varmints. They cut us folks in the colonies off from the rest of this country."

[67]

"How did you get over there?" Daniel asked eagerly. "Did you go through a gap in the mountains?"

"No, I went down the Ohio River, trading with the Injuns. The Injuns say there's a way through the mountains, though. They call that country over there Kentuck."

"Kentuck!" said Daniel softly. That land beyond the tall blue hills! And here was a man who had been there!

"What's it like?" he asked Mr. Finley. "Is it good country?"

Mr. Finley's eyes lighted with enthusiasm. "You never saw the like. Flat country. Flat as a man's hand. And rich!"

Daniel listened, taking in every word. Oh, he knew that would be fine country beyond the mountains!

Mr. Finley went on. "And the meadows are a sight to see. Miles and miles of flat land, so rich the clover grows waist-high. And the buffalo! Man, you ought to see the herds of buffalo that graze over them meadows. Millions of them."

Night after night Daniel sat by the campfire and talked with his new friend about Kentuck. About the buffalo and deer and beaver to be found there. Daniel knew he had to cross those mountains. Somehow he had to get down into that wonderful land.

"After this fight, let's you and me team up and go to Kentuck," he said to Finley once. "Let's find that way through the mountains."

"It'll be hard traveling through those mountains," said Mr. Finley. "And it'll be danger-

[69]

ous. Kentuck is the Injuns' hunting ground. They won't welcome us on it."

"We can do it," Daniel exclaimed. "We *got* to do it."

"Then we will do it," said Mr. Finley, and he clapped Daniel on the shoulder.

At last Braddock's army began its slow journey toward the French fort. Woodsmen went ahead cutting a road so the wagons could bring up the army's supplies.

Much to Daniel's disappointment he was not used as a scout. Instead he was ordered to drive one of the supply wagons. He didn't like the job, but he had volunteered to help. So he stayed with the wagon.

"Anyway," he said to himself. "I'll be with John Finley, if I stick with the wagons."

Kentuck! Was there ever such a fine land, thought Daniel. Day after day as he followed the British army through the forest, he thought about Kentuck. Every night he and Finley talked over plans about how to get there.

The days passed, but Daniel hardly knew one from the other.

One day he was driving along the newly cut

road in the line of wagons. The army was ahead of the wagons.

"Get up there, you no-good, corn-eating rascal," Boone called as he stood up and flicked his whip at one of his four horses. "Go on there."

Suddenly from ahead came the sound of guns and war whoops.

"What's going on?" Daniel cried.

He reached for his rifle, which was in the wagon beside him. The firing came closer. Then through the woods and down the wagon road ran British soldiers.

Someone yelled, "The Injuns are coming! Run for your life!"

Then Daniel saw painted warriors hurtling toward him through the trees.

Indians! Hundreds of them!

CHAPTER SIX

Over the Blue Ridge Mountains

A MAN rode by on one of his wagon horses. The slashed wagon traces flew out behind the animal.

"Run!" yelled the man to Daniel. "The Indians have ambushed us and the British Army is running."

The guns grew louder. Other men passed Daniel on foot and on horseback. "Get away while you can," they called. "The British are beaten!"

Daniel pulled on his reins. Indians were swarming toward him, shooting horses and setting fire to wagons as they came. Most of the red-coated British soldiers were fleeing in front of them. Here and there a few of the colonies' militia troops were trying to make a stand against the savages.

Daniel thought for a minute that he might be able to turn his wagon. The road was wide here. But the four horses were frightened. They reared and bumped into each other, not hearing Daniel's shouted commands.

Hastily Daniel jumped out of the wagon. He pulled his knife from its sheath and quickly cut the leather lines that held the horses together.

He sprang to the back of the nearest horse. The animal reared and suddenly an Indian seized the bridle. Daniel knocked the brave's hand away from the leather straps with the butt of his rifle. Another blow into the Indian's chest sent the savage staggering backward into the bushes.

There was a wild shriek as another Indian charged Daniel with upraised tomahawk. Quickly Daniel blocked the blow of the tomahawk with his rifle. At the same time he planted his foot full in the Indian's face and pushed with all his might. His moccasin came off as his horse leaped down the road.

It was all Daniel could do to stay on. He flattened himself along the horse's back and

[73]

held onto its mane. With his other hand he gripped his rifle.

The forest on each side of the road seemed full of Indians. Their war cries and the sound of guns made a deafening noise. The white men fled on all sides.

Daniel passed wagon after wagon filled with supplies and abandoned to the red men.

His horse splashed through a creek and thundered on along the rough road. Daniel thought it would be safe to stop now, but he could not control the horse. A mile or so farther on, the animal began to slow down.

As the horse began to go more slowly, Daniel caught glimpses of groups of red-coated British soldiers and militia men in buckskins gathered in the woods.

Finally the horse stopped. Daniel slid to the ground and patted the trembling creature.

One of the wagon drivers was standing near by. He spoke to Daniel. "I sure hate to run from a good fight. But there warn't anything else to do."

Daniel nodded. He hated to run from a fight too. But there were times when it had to be done. Running away from that battle would be what John Finley called "horse sense."

John Finley! Daniel wondered what had happened to his friend. He began to search the woods.

He saw a few British soldiers in torn coats, resting under the trees. Some of them had been

[75]

wounded and one had a bloody bandage on his head.

At the edge of a clearing was a group of men who belonged to the Virginia Militia. They were talking about their colonel, George Washington.

Daniel stopped to listen. He heard them tell how the Virginians had fought Indian style and Colonel Washington had gotten up from his sickbed and ridden into battle, trying to rally the fleeing British troops and get them behind trees and rocks. But the Indians were too many, and Washington and the Virginians fled with the rest.

Now Daniel saw a group of wagon drivers. "Have you seen John Finley?" he asked one.

"Finley?" the other asked. "Aye. His wagon was just ahead of mine before the redskins came. But I don't know what happened to him after that. He may not have gotten away. I don't know. I scarce got away myself."

Daniel turned away, discouraged. But he did not give up his search for his companion.

All the rest of that day he wandered among the soldiers and wagons. But by nightfall he had not found the other wagon driver. Daniel felt sure John Finley had been killed.

The defeated army was in full retreat. General Braddock had been killed. A large number of the British soldiers had been slain or captured. The expedition to take Fort Duquesne from the French had failed.

Daniel did not find John Finley, though he looked for him wherever he went.

In the fall Daniel returned to his home on the Yadkin River. There was still time left to hunt deer this season. He needed deerskins to buy supplies so he could search for the gap through the mountains to Kentuck. Even though Finley had disappeared, Daniel was not discouraged. There was a way through those mountains and he intended to find it.

Daniel had another reason for returning to the Yadkin. Just before he had left to go to the wars, Daniel had met a pretty black-eyed girl named Rebecca Bryan and he wanted to marry her.

The following summer Daniel and Rebecca became husband and wife. There was little time for a newly married man to explore the wilderness beyond the mountains. And he soon found that his deerskins were needed to buy household supplies and furnishings.

Later the Cherokee Indians went on the warpath. By this time Daniel and Rebecca had two little sons named James and Israel. Daniel knew that the wilderness where lurking Cherokees were looking for scalps was no place for a family man. He knew also that the frontier settlements along the Yadkin River were now in constant danger. So he stayed home to protect his wife and babies.

It was not until 1760 that Daniel was able to begin his explorations again. He was twenty-six that year and as tall and lanky and easy-going as ever.

And the hills still called to him. Every time he raised his eyes to those blue slopes, they seemed to beckon.

"Come on, Dan'l. Come see, come see!" they seemed to say.

One day he struck out for the Blue Ridge Mountains again, and crossed them into the land beyond, that was later to become Tennessee.

He was disappointed. This wasn't the land John Finley had described. There were no rolling meadows and open savannas here but only more valleys and hills, with more mountains farther to the west.

But there must be a way through those mountains. Somehow, a man and a horse could get through the rocky peaks and cliffs. He'd have to find the gaps, the low places and easy climbs that would lead through the mountains to the rich land on the other side.

Hunting was good, however. Up one valley and into another Daniel went, following the tracks of deer and bear.

One warm day, Daniel lay on a creek bank, staring up through the bare branches of the trees at the blue sky above. A squirrel scolded from across the creek.

"Now you hush up," said Daniel. "I've had my dinner and I ain't fixing to harm you. Let's just set here peaceable and enjoy ourselves. Ain't nobody but us for miles and miles."

Suddenly there was a startling sound of voices and laughter. Daniel sat up quickly.

"I was wrong, young feller," he whispered

to the squirrel. He crawled up the creek bank.
"When them Injuns come, tell them I was took
sick sudden and went home."

Daniel moved softly toward a cave he had
seen that morning. Here he knew he would be
safe. At the entrance he crouched, watching
the woods before him.

On came the Indians. Daniel thought they
must be Cherokees. Although these Indians
were supposed to be at peace with the colonies
now, he knew they would take the scalp of any
lone white man found hunting on their lands.

Quietly Daniel backed farther into the cave.
All at once behind him he heard a low growl.

He felt his spine tingle. A bear!

CHAPTER SEVEN

John Finley Again

FOR a moment Daniel squatted in the blackness of the cave, too surprised to stir. He could hear the snarling bear padding toward him.

Quickly he moved toward the cave entrance. The Indians were disappearing through the trees. But he knew that if he turned to shoot the bear, the sound of his gun would bring them running back.

Ducking out of the cave, he hid behind a big boulder. The bear followed him, growling angrily. Daniel dodged around the boulder and ran upstream in the direction opposite to that which had been taken by the Indians. The bear loped right behind him.

Daniel sped off among the rocks and bushes. Finally he said aloud, "By thunderation! I'm tired of running from this bear. This here country is just as much mine as it is his. And I'm willing to fight for it."

A big beech tree was just ahead.

"I'll jump behind this beech tree and shoot him," he said to himself. "Once the critters over here in this country find out this bear made Daniel Boone run for his life, why, all the varmints in creation will be chasing me to see my shirttail flap in the breeze. I won't put up with it!"

From behind the tree he raised his rifle, took aim, and squeezed the trigger.

Bang! The gun roared in the silence of the forest, echoing against the hills.

"If that don't bring them Injuns a-running, nothing will," Daniel said.

The bear was dead. Daniel slipped off among the trees and hid. He would take no chances with the Cherokees.

But they did not return, and later Daniel felt it was safe to come out of hiding. He skinned the bear and ate toasted bear toes for his dinner. Then he wiped his mouth with the sleeve of his hunting shirt.

"That was a fine meal," he said aloud, for he often talked to himself in the woods.

"I wonder how Rebecca is making out with our two young 'uns. I'd best make tracks for home, I reckon. But first I think I'll just let the critters and other folks know that I ain't to be trifled with. I'll just leave a little message for them."

He walked up to the beech tree under which he had killed the bear. Finding a smooth place, he began to cut into the bark with his knife.

Finally he stepped back to read his inscription.

D. Boon
Cilled A. Bar on
Tree
in the
year
1760

"There," he murmured. "My sister Elizabeth ought to see that. That's good enough spelling for anybody. And beech trees grow mighty slow. That'll be there for a long time."

He picked up his rifle and started through the Blue Ridge for home. Once again he had failed to find the way to Kentuck. But he'd be patient. And he was bound to find it one of these days.

If only John Finley hadn't disappeared.

Daniel thought back to those nights around the campfire, when he had listened to Finley's tales of buffalo so thick you couldn't stir them with a stick, and woods full of so many deer, they begged hunters to shoot them.

Daniel longed to see such a land. The years passed and he roamed through the woods and

[84]

He began to cut into the bark with his knife

in the valleys to the west, hunting, and searching for Kentuck.

His family grew larger. Six children filled the Boone cabin. Daniel wanted to move once more. He needed more land and fewer neighbors. He was a hunter, not a farmer. Now new settlers were driving the deer farther west. When deer got scarce, times were hard for the Boones.

One day in the year 1769, Daniel strode into his clearing on the Yadkin, leading his pack horse.

"Here's Pa, now," yelled his son James. He ran to meet his father. "Pa, we got company for the supper meal."

"Let me tell him," begged Jemima. "Pa, a trader fellow's here. You ought to see the ribbons he's got."

Daniel laughed as his children gathered around him, shouting to be heard. He gave James his horse's lead rope. He put Levina on his shoulders.

Israel took his rifle. Susannah and Jemima danced beside him as he walked toward the cabin.

[*86*]

"There, you no-good young 'uns. I see you need a good frolic," Daniel said. "After supper I'll just wrassle you in knots."

Then he looked up to see a man watching him from the cabin door. The visitor looked familiar.

Daniel stared. He couldn't believe his eyes. After fourteen years!

It was John Finley!

CHAPTER EIGHT

Kentuck at Last

Aᴏ FTER supper that night Boone threw a big log on the fire. Then he sat down with Baby Rebecca in his arms.

"Well, John," he said, "it's been a long time since we were with Braddock, hasn't it?"

"Yes, Dan'l, but you don't look any older," chuckled Finley. "If anything, younger."

Daniel laughed. "Hear that, Becky?" he called to his wife, who was washing the wooden trenchers and horn spoons. "John thinks I'm as handsome now at thirty-five as I was at twenty-one."

Rebecca Boone smiled at her husband. With his sandy hair, his hooked nose and wide mouth, Daniel couldn't be called handsome. But his eyes were bright blue and clear. He was tall and strong-looking. Rebecca was proud of him. She turned to the trader.

"Mr. Finley," she said, "I hope you'll show Dan'l the way into Kentuck before he drives us all daft."

"He don't drive me daft," spoke up James. "I aim to go with him."

Daniel grinned at his small son and rumpled his long hair. "That's right, James, you take up for your pa."

[89]

Mr. Finley took a wood splinter from the fire and lighted his pipe.

"Mrs. Boone, that be the very thing I want to talk to your husband about. I been thinking about going back to Kentuck, but I need a man who knows his way in the woods."

Finley puffed slowly on his pipe.

"A couple of years ago, I reckon it was, I was over there doing some trading. I floated down the Ohio River and went into Kentuck that way. But the Indians told me where to find the trail through the mountains. This here trail is called the Warrior's Path and they use it all the time. I aim to find it, if you'll help me, Dan'l."

Boone was ready to help. He persuaded his brother-in-law, John Stuart, and three other men to go with them. He got his brother, Squire Boone, to promise to bring supplies out to them early in the winter, and said he and the others would blaze a trail for Squire to follow. And he arranged with Judge Richard Henderson of Salisbury to furnish them with horses and powder and lead. In return, Daniel agreed to bring information back to Judge Henderson about the wonderful new country.

[*90*]

Everybody was satisfied with the arrangements Boone made. In May, 1769, six men set out from Daniel's cabin on the Yadkin River.

As he left the clearing, Daniel turned to wave to his family.

"Find us a good piece of farm land, Dan'l," his wife called.

"Kill a buffalo for me, Pa," James yelled.

Daniel laughed. His family thought about Kentuckee as much as he did himself. With a final wave of his hand he walked away.

This time he was going to get to Kentuck!

Over the Blue Ridge Mountains and through the wilderness the six men journeyed. And one day they hit a well-worn trail that led through a gap in the mountains.

Was this the way through the mountains that the Indians had told John Finley about?

At the top of the gap the sweating, tired men stopped. The mountains rose tall on each side of them, but still they were high enough to look down into the valley below. It didn't look as wonderful as Boone had thought it would. But John Finley was excited.

"This is it. It's the gap we've been searching

for. That trail must be the Warrior's Path the Indians told me about. Come on!"

Daniel Boone and his party had found Cumberland Gap. They were not the first men to go through the gap into Kentuck.

Other men had chanced upon the gap, used it once and forgotten about it. But not Daniel Boone. He would not forget. Cumberland Gap was going to mean a lot to Boone and to the colonies that would later win their independence and become the United States of America.

Kentuck proved to be all Finley had said. The country was teeming with game. For months the six men hunted. They ate well. There were no Indians around.

Life was pleasant and their piles of skins grew larger. They were getting richer every day they stayed in Kentuck.

Daniel was beginning to think there wasn't an Indian in the whole land of Kentuckee. His eyes took in everything in the woods. Yet he had seen no sign of them.

"John," he said to Stuart one winter morning, "I'm mighty put out with the Injuns. They don't seem to like Kentuck."

John grinned. He liked Daniel and he liked to hunt with him. "I reckon they're sitting at home, counting their scalps. Let's go shoot some more buffalo while the redskins are warming by the fire."

Boone was in the lead when they started out from their camp. The sun was shining from a warm December sky. High overhead a buzzard circled lazily. Near by a loon called its lonesome cry.

"It's a jim-dandy day to hunt," Daniel commented.

[93]

'Almost like spring,'' his brother-in-law answered.

They passed a canebrake. The tall stalks of cane rustled in the breeze. Tall copper-colored figures rose up silently, stepped out of the canebrake, and stood before the hunters.

Boone stopped. He smiled and threw up his hand. "Howdy," he said in his quiet. pleasant voice. "How's the hunting this morning?"

Neither of the white men showed any sign of surprise. Without a word the Shawnee Indians closed in around the two men, who now

had no chance to escape. Tall and straight, the chief stood before Boone and stared into the hunter's eyes.

Boone stared back. For a long time the two looked silently at each other. At last the chief said, "Me, Captain Will."

Daniel pretended to be delighted to meet the Indian and shook his hand. "I'm Dan'l Boone," he answered. "This here is John Stuart. Me and him's just looking around."

The chief grunted, "Where camp?"

Boone shrugged his shoulders. He didn't want to show these Indians their camp. All the months he and his friends had spent hunting would count for nothing, for the red men would take all their skins and furs.

Suddenly the chief reached out and snatched Daniel's rifle from his hand. Another Shawnee took Stuart's gun.

The chief leveled the gun at Daniel. "Show camp," he commanded.

"Looks like he's got you, Dan'l," Stuart said behind him. "Better show him."

"Why, I aimed to show him all the time. Captain Will's a fine fellow. I like him," Dan-

The chief reached out and snatched Daniel's rifle

iel remarked with a smile. "This way, Chief."

Boone led the way back to the camp. All the way there he talked in a loud voice, so the other white hunters would hear him and have time to hide themselves and the skins.

But when they reached the camp, Daniel was dismayed to find all the skins and supplies and the horses in plain view. There was no sign of the other hunters.

Captain Will looked over the skins. He turned to Boone. "Skins belong to red man," he said. He gave orders to the other Indians in the Shawnee language. They began to pile the skins together. The chief turned back to Daniel.

"This Injun land," he said with a sweep of his arm. "Deer Injun. Bear Injun. Not white man's. Go home. Not come here to hunt."

The braves worked swiftly. Soon the skins were loaded on the white men's horses. Then with a grunt, Captain Will led the pack horses away.

Daniel watched silently. He had hoped to take his share of those skins back to Salisbury and to pay off some of his debts.

[98]

"There goes seven months' hard work," remarked Stuart bitterly as the Indians disappeared. "It's enough to make a fellow give up."

"By thunder, they ain't quite gone yet. We'll follow those red varmints," said Boone. "Them skins may be Injun skins, but I aim to have our horses back. Come on."

He slipped off into the brush beside the trail. Stuart followed him. They soon caught up with the Indians. All that day they trailed the red men, keeping under cover just behind them.

Late in the afternoon the Indians made camp beside a spring. They unloaded the skins, tied up the horses, and made a fire. After their meal they stretched out beside the fire and were soon snoring loudly. One Indian had been left as a guard, but he nodded sleepily too.

Boone nudged Stuart. Crawling on their stomachs, the two made their way to where the horses were tied. One of the animals neighed softly. The guard awoke and glanced in that direction.

The two men dropped behind a log and

waited. After a while Daniel peered around the log and found the guard dozing again.

Quickly he was on his feet cutting the ropes that held the horses. He sprang to the back of one horse and leading two others, rode quietly past the guard. Stuart was right behind him on another horse and leading still another.

The rest of the night they rode toward the south. Finally at dawn Daniel called a halt. "I reckon we've put enough miles between us and Captain Will so's we can stop a bit," he said as he dismounted.

They hobbled the horses by a canebrake and lay down to sleep near by. Boone had hardly shut his eyes before he was seized roughly by the shoulders. Once more he was face to face with Captain Will.

With a smile, he jumped up. "Howdy, Captain Will," he said, shaking the chief's hand. "I'm delighted to see you again."

Captain Will grimaced and growled, "Steal horse, ha. Me show you."

He told his men to tie Stuart to a tree. Then he placed a horse-bell around Daniel's neck.

"You dance," he ordered.

Boone was frightened, but he did not show

it. He knew his only chance for escape lay in not letting the Indians know he was afraid and making them laugh.

The braves gathered about him, grinning and nudging one another.

Daniel looked around at them, and then grinned at Stuart. "All right," he said. "I like to dance. But I guess I'll have to furnish my own music."

He began to shuffle his feet. The bell around his neck tinkled and Boone danced faster. He

[*101*]

threw back his head and sang in a loud, merry voice:

"I don't want none of your weevily wheat;
    I don't want none of your barley;
  I want the finest of wheat
    To bake a cake for Charley."

While he sang, he stamped his feet and kicked out his legs. First this way, then that. The bell rang gaily.

The Indians laughed and yelled encouragement to him. Even Stuart, tied to the tree, watched Daniel with a smile.

Finally Daniel was winded and stopped.

"Me like. Good dance," said Captain Will, taking the bell from Boone's neck.

That night Daniel was tied to a tree too. As soon as the Indians were asleep, however, he managed to cut the deer thongs which bound him. He freed Stuart, too, and the two men ran off through the darkness.

Suddenly behind them came a loud yell. One of the Indians had wakened and discovered that they had gone.

"Run for your life, John," Boone panted. "If they get us again, they'll kill us for sure!"

CHAPTER NINE

Lone Hunter

BOONE and Stuart raced along a creek bank, stumbling over bushes and rocks. It was hard to run in the dark. Low-hanging branches slapped their faces. They ran into trees. But behind them they heard the Indians pursuing them closely.

Finally Daniel called breathlessly, "Here, John, we'll hide in the canebrake. They'll never find us."

The cane grew thick and tall. The dry leaves rattled as the white men pushed their way deep into the brake.

"This is far enough," panted Daniel.

The two men sat down, exhausted. They stayed hidden there all night. The Indians searched around the canebrake and once came within a few yards of the hunters. At daylight however, the Shawnees gave up the search and left.

Boone and Stuart started at once for their camp. They reached the place some hours later and found it was still deserted.

Stuart was angry. "They got no right to leave us like this," he exclaimed.

"I reckon they thought we was dead and they started for home," said Boone. He wasn't angry. He was in the woods without horse or food or gun, but he was as calm and easygoing as ever.

By following the footprints and broken branches left by the hurrying men, Boone and Stuart soon caught up with Finley and his companions.

"We'd given you up. Thought you were gone goslings," said Finley. He turned to Daniel. "Me and these fellows have had enough. All our months of work have gone into Injun hands. We're leaving Kentuck, while we still got our hair anyway."

Daniel nodded. He knew how the others felt. Their whole winter's hunt was gone. And they were afraid. They wanted to get back to their homes and families.

But after all these years of trying to get to Kentuck, Boone wouldn't leave so easily. He'd stay to look around. He'd try to get more skins to pay off those debts to Judge Henderson.

He told John Finley, "Go home then. Your scalp's your own to take care of. But me and Stuart will stay till Squire comes. Give us each a rifle and powder and lead, and we'll stay."

Boone and John Stuart were very careful after the other men had gone, and had no further trouble with the Indians. When Squire Boone followed Daniel's blazed tree trail into Kentuck early in the winter, he found the two men near their camp waiting for him. Squire brought supplies on his pack horses. He also brought news that Rebecca and the children were well. And he told Daniel that he had decided to stay in Kentuck for a while to hunt and look around.

Late one afternoon the following spring, John Stuart failed to return to camp.

"Reckon John's in trouble?" Squire asked his brother.

"Won't be the first time, I reckon," answered Daniel. "If he don't come in by morning, we'll look for him."

Stuart was still missing the next morning. Daniel was worried. He set out following Stuart's trail. At a creek he lost the tracks. He and Squire searched the creek banks on both sides, but they could not pick up the trail again.

"John's been like a brother to me, Squire," Daniel said that night, as he and Squire sat close to their fire. "Me and him have had some narrow escapes. I reckon danger makes fellows close to each other."

Squire spoke. "Maybe he'll show up before I leave."

"I hope so," replied Daniel.

Two months later in May when Squire loaded the skins on the horses, John Stuart still had not come back.

"You won't stay here in Kentuckee now, will you, Dan'l?" asked Squire.

"I aim to. I'm used to my own company and I reckon I can stand it," Daniel answered. "Besides, I told Judge Henderson I would explore Kentuck for him. And I ain't looked around near enough."

Squire didn't say anything. Daniel had been taking care of himself in the woods since he was a tad back in Pennsylvania. Squire wouldn't worry about him.

"Well, take care of yourself, Dan'l. I'll be back right here by the end of summer if all goes well."

"All right, Squire. Give my love to Rebecca and the young 'uns. Fare thee well."

Squire rode off, leading the pack horses. He left his brother alone in the middle of the wilderness. Daniel had not even a dog or a horse for companionship. He was without salt or bread.

But he was happy, as he hunted and explored. He was not worried at all. He knew he could take care of himself no matter what happened.

In the months that followed Daniel roamed far and wide in Kentucky. He explored down the Licking River. He went down the Ohio River as far as its falls.

He came up the Kentucky River valley. He

looked for good springs and cabin sites. He hid at salt licks and watched the game. Animals came to these springs to drink the salt water or lick the salty earth. Salt was a necessary part of their diet.

One day Boone lay in the tall grass on a slope, looking at a herd of buffalo below him. They were wallowing in the mudholes around a spring.

Daniel watched a great shaggy bull. It had taken a mudhole for its very own. Every time another buffalo approached, the bull bellowed and drove it away. Then the bull lay down in the mud and rolled back and forth.

Suddenly something frightened the herd. The great bull was out of the mudhole in a flash. The other beasts closed up behind him. With a bellow the bull led the buffaloes straight up the slope toward Boone.

Daniel sprang to his feet and began to run toward the trees some distance away. He knew he would be trampled to death if the buffaloes reached him.

On they came, thundering close behind him. The earth shook with their great weight as they pounded up the hill. Boone knew now that he would never make the woods. He would have to save himself some other way.

Quickly he stopped and turned.

Raising his rifle, he fired at the huge leader, which was bearing down on him with lowered head. For one awful moment he didn't know whether he had hit the animal or not.

The leader charged on, with the herd right behind him. Daniel gave himself up for lost.

Then the bull stumbled, lost his footing, and fell a few feet from where Daniel stood. Boone ran toward him and threw himself on the ground behind the body of the dead buffalo.

The rest of the herd split in two groups and went around the body of their leader. Daniel Boone was safe. Once again his steady hand, sure eye, and quick thinking had saved his life.

"Well," he said, getting to his feet as the buffalo disappeared. "I reckon I might get back home yet to see Becky and the tads. And to tell Judge Henderson this is the finest land in all creation. But that was close, mighty close."

[*109*]

He took out his knife and began to skin the bull buffalo.

Boone stayed in the wilderness until the following spring, almost two years altogether. When he finally returned to Salisbury, he told Judge Henderson what he had seen in the land beyond the mountains.

"Somebody ought to open up that country," he told the judge. "It's fine farming land. Folks would flock there. And the men who

went in first and started settlements and made land claims could make a heap of money selling land to people who came later."

"Yes," Richard Henderson agreed. "It would be a wonderful thing. I'd like to do it.

But I can't while I'm a judge. I'll have to wait till I'm a private citizen again, and that may be a few years yet."

But Daniel did not want to wait. He wanted to live in Kentuck right away. So he sold his farm on the Yadkin River and everything he owned. He talked some of his friends into going with him and taking along their families. They were going to a place Boone had chosen on the Kentucky River as a good spot for a settlement.

But on the way to Kentucky the Indians attacked them and several of the settlers were killed. James Boone, Daniel and Rebecca's oldest son, was one of those who died.

The settlers were so discouraged and saddened that they turned back to the North Carolina settlements. The Boones were heartbroken. They had no home now. They had lost many of their cows and horses, and their handsome, brave young son was dead.

Daniel and his family went to live with friends on the Clinch River in Virginia. Rebecca begged her husband not to try to settle in Kentuck again.

"Those Injuns didn't attack us because we

were trying to settle in Kentuck," Daniel Boone argued. "They were just plain ornery. They'd have killed anybody they met anywhere."

"But it's plain to see the Injuns don't want us on their hunting lands," said Mrs. Boone. "As long as they own that country, they think white people ought not to come there."

Boone nodded. "I reckon so," he told his wife. "It might be safer to live in Kentuck if the Injuns sold the land. The Cherokees claim they own Kentuck. Perhaps they'll sell it to someone who can pay a fine price for it. I'll go to Salisbury and talk to Judge Henderson."

He went once more to see Richard Henderson, who was no longer a judge. Henderson listened carefully to what Boone had to say.

"Dan'l, I believe you're right," he told the woodsman. "If the land was bought from the Indians in a proper legal way, a colony could be started on the rich land of Kentuck." He paused. "If some of my friends and I form a land company and raise enough money to buy Kentuck, do you think the Cherokees will sell it?" he asked.

[*113*]

"I'll find out for you, if you want me to," Boone replied.

So Henderson sent Daniel out to talk to the chiefs of the Cherokee tribe. The Cherokees had never lived in Kentuck. They had used the land only for hunting. They agreed to sell it, and Henderson invited them all to a place called Sycamore Shoals to discuss the price.

CHAPTER TEN

Boonesborough

————————————————

I RECKON the whole Cherokee nation must be here," Richard Henderson said to Daniel Boone on a March day of 1775.

Daniel looked around. The Watauga River swirled over the shoals and rocks, and a cold wind whipped through the sycamore trees along the riverbank.

Under the trees stood hundreds of Indian shelters made of bark and brush. In a clearing, women were cooking meat. Whole bear and deer and beefs sent up delicious smells.

Among the cooking pits moved the Cherokees. There were braves in bright blankets and red cloth, as well as the Indian women in calico dresses. Boone thought they made a bright, pretty picture.

[*115*]

"I reckon they wouldn't miss this for anything, Judge," Daniel said. "I just hope nothing stirs 'em up. They could wipe out the Watauga settlements—"

"Hush!" interrupted the judge. "Here comes the Little Carpenter."

The Indian coming toward them was a tiny old man with a wrinkled, kindly face. He was Attakullakulla, the Little Carpenter, a chief of the Cherokees.

He and the other Cherokees had come to Sycamore Shoals to examine the cabin full of guns, shirts, blankets, knives, and trinkets which the judge was offering in exchange for their land.

Attakullakulla smiled at Boone. "How do, Brother," he said.

Then he turned to Richard Henderson. "How do, Carolina Dick. You fine fellow. Big cabin full of goods. Braves like. Women like. We talk now."

"Fine!" exclaimed Judge Henderson.

He drew Boone aside. "Dan'l, get your men ready. You might as well start now cutting that road. It may take a few days for all the chiefs

[*116*]

to sign the deed, but there'll be no trouble."

Boone was ready. He had hired a number of men to help him. These men were strong and skilled in woodcraft. They were used to hard work and danger. With their axes they would make a trail through the mountains.

Daniel rode to where his party of men waited. "The judge says for us to start," he told them. "I'll lay out the way and you come behind me and cut out the bushes."

Daniel Boone was building his Wilderness Road, the road over which the pioneers would go to Kentucky.

He connected buffalo paths with Indian trails. The men followed, cutting and hacking their way through valleys and over mountains. They chopped down trees and cleared away brush.

Through Cumberland Gap the party went and along the Warrior's Path, as they pushed toward the wide meadows of Kentucky.

One day a worker found a skeleton. It was lying in a hollow sycamore tree and a powder horn lay by its side. The horn bore the initials, J.S.

Daniel knew that these must be the bones of his brother-in-law, John Stuart. It made him sad, but he had no time to grieve. There was work to be done.

When the road builders finally arrived at the Kentucky River, they chopped down trees and built a few cabins. They decided to name the place for their leader.

"Well, Dan'l," said Michael Stoner, looking at the six finished cabins, "we've begun the settlement of Boonesborough."

[*118*]

"It's begun, I reckon," Boone answered his old friend. "But it won't be done with till Rebecca and the young 'uns come here to live. And I aim to get 'em here as soon as I can."

Boone journeyed back over the mountains for his family. He reached the cabin late one afternoon.

Israel was chopping wood in the clearing in front of the cabin. He looked up and saw his father.

"Here's Pa," he called to the others.

The Boone children ran from the cabin. Rebecca stood smiling in the doorway, watching the children swarm around their father.

"Are we going to Kentuck, Pa?" asked young Rebecca.

"Did you cut the road to Kentuck, Pa?" Daniel Morgan wanted to know.

"Did you get us a cabin built?" Levina questioned.

Daniel shouted, "Yes, yes!" to all the questions and strode inside the cabin. "Rebecca, get ready," he said. "I aim to take you to the best land in all creation."

Rebecca Boone looked startled. "Are we

going right now?" she asked, looking out the door at the gathering darkness. "Dan'l, it's too late today to start packing."

Daniel laughed. "We're not goin' right away, I reckon." He looked toward the hearth where the iron pot hung over the wood fire. "I'm too hungry to start back now. How about some of that stew first?"

Daniel had many things to do in the settlement and two months passed before the Boones were ready to move. One August morning they were up before daybreak. After a hurried breakfast of cold ash cake and stew left over from the night before, the packing began by firelight.

"Israel," ordered his father, "get the horses around to the front of the cabin." He turned to his daughter. "Jemima, go turn the cows out and let them graze till we get ready to leave. Maybe if they start with full stomachs they won't hold us up by stopping to eat every step of the way."

Young Daniel Morgan ran excitedly up to his mother with the three-legged stool. "Ma, can we take this?" he asked.

Jesse, the baby, tottered across the floor to his mother with the turkey wing that was used to sweep the ashes off the hearth. "Take this," he shouted.

Mrs. Boone laughed and held up her hands. "If we take everything, it'll take a wagon to fetch us there."

Daniel looked around. "A wagon can't get over my road," he said. "It'll be hard enough to get to Kentuck on horseback. In a few years maybe the road will be good enough to bring a wagon over."

A cow mooed outside. Israel called, "The horses are ready, Pa."

"Rebecca, you fold up the coverlids," Mrs. Boone told her daughter. "We'll take them and the skillets and pots. Your pa can make us new beds and a table and stools when we get to Kentuck."

Everyone worked hard, carrying out deerskin bags of cornmeal and salt, gourds full of gunpowder, and the Boones' few clothes of buckskin and homespun.

Rebecca carried an armload of quilts to her father, who tied them on the back of one of the horses with leather thongs and straps. The cooking pans were tied on another. A third horse carried bars of lead and the gunpowder.

By the time the sun rose, the Boones were ready to go. Mrs. Boone came out of the cabin with the baby in her arms. "I'm ready, Dan'l," she said.

"Yippee!" shouted young Daniel Morgan. "We're off to Kentuck!"

Daniel helped Mrs. Boone up on a horse. The children were to take turns riding one of the other horses. They would walk for the most part. But they were used to walking.

"We'll meet the men folks who are going with us at the fork of the trail," Daniel said. He walked ahead with his rifle.

Israel jerked on the lead rope and the horses followed after him. The Boones were off to Kentuck!

About two weeks later the party of pioneers stood on the small hill that looked down on Boonesborough.

"See yonder, Rebecca," Daniel pointed. "That's our cabin."

Mrs. Boone stood quietly looking down at the six rough log cabins. Smoke trailed into the air from two of the chimneys. One of the Boone cows mooed and began to eat the grass.

"Boonesborough ain't very big," commented Jemima from beside her mother.

"Not yet," answered Boone. "Everything starts out little, I reckon. But it'll grow. The rich land here is bound to bring folks."

"Pa," shouted Daniel Morgan. "Where're the Injuns? I don't see none."

Boone looked at his six-year-old son. "The Injuns'll come here without an invitation, Dan'l Morgan. Come on, let's get the first white women folks to come to Boonesborough down to their new home."

The group moved slowly down the grassy slope toward the few cabins.

CHAPTER ELEVEN

Indians at Boonesborough

————————————————————

IT WAS a year later. A good many families had come to Boonesborough to settle. Cabins were springing up all about, and a strong wooden stockade stood on a hill. Some of the cabins were enclosed in the stockade, but others were not.

Fields and gardens had been cleared and planted. Cows were pastured in the near-by meadows and chickens pecked in the clearings. Everything seemed peaceful and prosperous.

But trouble was on the way for the people of Boonesborough. Indeed, it had already come to most Americans.

Even before the Boones had moved to Kentucky, the Revolutionary War had begun. It had started because the King of England had been ruling his American colonies very badly. Thousands of Americans had decided that they could not put up with such treatment any longer. There had already been bitter fighting between the colonists and red-coated English soldiers.

Daniel and his family did not know much about this. It was only from new settlers that Boone learned that the thirteen colonies had declared they would no longer be ruled by England, and that Congress had issued a Declaration of Independence.

Daniel agreed with his countrymen that the colonies need not be told what to do by England and that it was time they were free from the mother country. But he was too far away from the fighting to keep up with events.

As the leader of Boonesborough, he was worried about the Indian tribes which lived north of the Ohio River. These tribes traded with the British and were siding with them against the Americans.

There were other settlements in Kentuck. Harrodsburg and Logan's Station were about forty miles west of Boonesborough. Daniel knew the different settlements would have to help each other if the Indians should attack in force.

Months passed and the Indians did attack, but only in small parties of a few braves. These warriors hid in the bushes near the springs and on the edges of cornfields. They attacked women coming for water, or men going out to hoe the crops. Sometimes a man who went out to hunt never came back to the fort again, and the others knew the savages had captured or killed him.

The people in the Kentucky settlements grew frightened. No one knew how many Indians might be hiding in the forests. Some of the settlers left Boonesborough and went back to their former homes. But others decided that if Daniel Boone and his wife and children were staying, they'd stay with them.

One morning in the spring of 1777, a family of settlers arrived at Boonesborough just as Daniel was sending scouts out of the fort to look for Indians.

"You Mr. Boone?" asked a tall man who was leading a horse.

"That's me," answered Daniel. "Be ye aiming to settle here?"

"I was aiming to," the stranger replied. "But I met a man down the trail a piece. He said he was leaving Boonesborough and going back to Caroliny. Said you all were having a heap of trouble with the Injuns. I don't know as I want to bring my family into a place where you're having Injun trouble."

"Well, we've had some Injun fights," remarked Daniel. "Just enough to keep a fellow's shooting-hand in. But this is mighty good land hereabouts. And there's plenty of it. It's worth fighting for."

"We come from our home in New Jersey because we were sick of fighting. The British were whipping everybody in sight," the man said. He looked around at his wife and his family of children, as if wondering where in the world he could take them where they would be safe.

Daniel frowned. "We're going to have to fight the British till the colonies get their independence," he stated. "It's the British that keep these Injuns stirred up against us. They furnish the Injuns with powder and lead, and horses, and even men. And they pay money for American scalps and prisoners."

"Why, the dirty dogs!" exclaimed the new-comer angrily. "But I heard tell that Judge Henderson bought this land from the Injuns fair and square. Is that so?"

"Aye," Daniel nodded. "But Judge Henderson bought the land from the Cherokees. Now these Injun tribes north of the Ohio

[129]

River claim that Kentuck was their hunting land too. So they are going to fight for it. But I reckon they wouldn't do much fighting if the British didn't keep them stirred up."

"Well, I'll be danged!" the stranger almost shouted. "I'll stay! I'll stay and fight the Injuns and show these tarnal Britishers that Americans are tough enough to fight red men and white men too. We'll be independent yet!"

The newcomer was soon to have a chance to prove that he meant what he said. One warm April morning Boone sat at the table in his cabin. Jemima had just set a trencher of ash cake on the puncheon table.

"Thank ye, Jemima," Daniel said. He broke off a piece of the bread and ate it. "You make ash cake well nigh as good as your ma."

"You're just hungry, Pa. Anybody's bread would taste good to you this morning," Jemima replied, laughing.

She looked around suddenly at the sound of shots.

Boone sprang to his feet. "Start molding some bullets, Jemima," he said. "It's Injuns, I reckon."

[*130*]

He grabbed his rifle, powder horn, and shot bag, and ran from the cabin. Other men appeared with their rifles. Women hurried the children inside the fort.

A man shouted from the stockade gate. "Hurry! Injuns have shot Jacob Trent and are making for the woods!"

When Boone reached the open gate, he saw a few Indians among the trees at the bottom of the hill. Simon Kenton, his scout, was helping Jacob Trent to the fort.

"Don't look like many, let's give 'em a fight, boys," Daniel called out to the others.

Boone and several other men ran through the clearing around the fort toward the spot where they had seen the Indians.

When the Boonesborough men had almost reached the bottom of the hill, Simon Kenton suddenly screamed from the fort, "Dan'l! Look out! More Injuns!"

Daniel looked over his shoulder. There were half a dozen braves behind him. He saw he had been outsmarted. The Indians had led him into a trap and cut him off from the fort.

"Boys, I've gotten you into a tight fix," Dan·

iel cried. "Sell your lives dear and fight like the very devil."

The pioneers rushed back toward the fort, straight at the Indians who had cut them off.

"Now," shouted Daniel, who was in the lead, "pick you out an Injun and let him have it."

He raised his own rifle and shot. Then he

charged, swinging his rifle as a club. The other men did the same.

An Indian waving a tomahawk rose up before Daniel. Boone whacked the brave in the head with his rifle, breaking the wooden stock. He drew his own tomahawk from his belt.

As he did so, an Indian ran up and jabbed his rifle hard against Boone's ankle. Pain shot up Daniel's leg. He fell to the ground, his ankle broken.

But he was not out of the fight. With his

tomahawk he slashed at every red figure in reach.

An Indian flung himself down on Daniel and wrestled his tomahawk from his hand. Boone tried to draw out his hunting knife, but the red man kicked it from his hand.

Boone struggled mightily. But now the brave had pinned him down. With a yell of triumph the Indian raised his bloody tomahawk!

CHAPTER TWELVE

Daniel Is Captured

SIMON KENTON rushed up. He poked his rifle into the Indian's back and pulled the trigger. The savage slumped forward on top of Boone.

Simon pushed the Indian away. He told Boone, "I'll carry you to the fort."

As he knelt to pick Daniel up, an Indian charged them.

Kenton jumped up and grabbed his rifle. Swinging it like a club, he knocked the Indian out. Then he picked Boone up in his arms and staggered toward the fort. A red man grabbed his arm. Simon jerked away.

The other settlers were fighting their way slowly toward the fort. Kenton stumbled ahead of them. Boone was heavy.

As he neared the stockade, a girl darted through the gate and ran toward him. "Git back," Simon panted.

But the girl came on. It was Jemima Boone. "Quick!" she said. "Put Pa down and let him lean on both of us. We can get him inside all right."

With Kenton on one side and Jemima on the other, helping him, Daniel reached the safety of the fort. Mrs. Boone tended to her husband while Simon went back to the fight. Soon the Indians were gone.

"Well, Simon, you're indeed a fine fellow," Daniel later remarked with a grin. "Thanks to you, I reckon I'll live to fight them Shawnees again." He winked at his daughter. "Jemima, you did yourself proud today. I reckon I'd better take you with me the next time I fight."

But Boone did very little fighting for a while. Even after he was up and limping around, he stayed close to Boonesborough.

There was plenty of work for Daniel to see to right there at home. Scouts had to be sent into the woods to watch for Indians. Men must be appointed to guard the cows while they

[136]

grazed. Trees had to be cut to use in strengthening the fort walls.

Ever since he had chosen the location for Boonesborough, Daniel had been the leader of the settlers. They looked to Boone for advice, for help, for courage. He knew Kentucky. He knew Indians. He knew what to do in any emergency. He was a natural leader and he accepted his responsibility.

Early in the following year, the salt supply at Boonesborough began to get low. Boone's ankle had healed now, so he and thirty men went to some salt springs called Blue Licks about fifty miles north of Boonesborough. With them went a pack train of horses, carrying supplies and the big pots for making salt.

At the Blue Licks the men filled the pots with water from the salt springs. Then huge fires were made under the pots. When the water boiled away, crystals of salt were left in the bottom. It was slow, hard work.

Boone kept the men supplied with meat, so they would not have to be away from the boiling pots.

One cold January day when they had been

at the salt springs nearly a month, Boone went
hunting. Snow lay on the ground. He knew
there was little chance of Indians lurking near.
During the winter months the red men usually
stayed close to the fires in their homes.

So Boone was considerably surprised to find
himself pursued through the snow by a small
party of Indians. When he saw he could not get
away, Boone gave himself up. He had escaped
from Indians when captured before. He would
do it this time too, he told himself.

Daniel gave the Indians his gun. "Howdy
do," he said. He shook hands with each of his
captors.

The Indians laughed with delight and were
glad to shake hands. They knew Daniel
Boone and had been outwitted by him often.
They were happy to have captured him now.

Boone talked and joked with them as they
took him toward their camp. But he watched
for an opportunity to escape.

When he reached the Indian camp he was
horrified to see more than a hundred painted
warriors seated around several fires. At once
he gave up thinking of his own fate, for he

[*138*]

realized that the people at Boonesborough and the men at the salt springs were in great danger. He knew that he must save them if he could. But how?

Boone recognized Blackfish, the chief of the Shawnee raiding party. These two had fought against each other many times.

The chief pointed at Daniel and laughed. Daniel laughed with him.

"Blackfish, howdy do. You're looking fine and sassy," Boone joked, knowing the other could not understand him.

Blackfish, who had a blanket drawn tightly around his squat figure, poked Daniel in the ribs. He said something in his language and all the Indians shouted with glee. The chief bent double with laughter.

"Bring out the fiddles," shouted Daniel. He still hoped that the Indians did not know about the salt-makers. He wanted the Shawnees to think he was unworried and happy to see them. "Let's have us a real jollification. Me and Blackfish will lead the reel."

He laughed and slapped his leg. Blackfish hit him on the back in a friendly fashion.

[*139*]

DANIEL BOONE

Finally an interpreter was brought. Blackfish took Daniel to the fire. The other Indians
returned to their fires, for the wind was cold.

Boone spoke to the interpreter. "Tell Blackfish I'm happy to see him again. And that I
hope he's well."

While they talked, Daniel saw some white
men at one of the fires. He knew then that this
was a raid planned by the British. Those men
at the fire were British Indian agents or British traders who had furnished the powder and
lead to the Indians and urged them to go on
the warpath.

It looked bad for the folks at Boonesborough. With almost all the men away making salt, the fort was unprotected. The women
and children would be taken captives. Boone
thought maybe he could warn the salt-makers
in some way.

The interpreter was speaking to him.
"Blackfish says he wants you to tell the people
at Boonesborough to give up. He also wants to
know who are the men making salt."

Boone did not blink an eye. He realized
there was no way now to save his own men

since Blackfish already knew where they were. Suddenly he decided on a bold plan.

"Tell Blackfish," Daniel said, "that the salt-makers are my men. Tell him I will get them to surrender without a fight if he promises not to torture them or make them run the gauntlet. Tell him it's too cold to move the women and children to the Indian towns now, but if Chief Blackfish will wait until spring I will tell Boonesborough to give up. Then he can have all my people and the fort without a fight."

Blackfish thought a moment after the interpreter translated this to him. Finally he agreed and shook Boone's hand.

Boone breathed a silent sigh of relief. He had saved the women and children of Boonesborough. He knew Blackfish would keep his word. And by next spring the fort would have help and would never give up. He had thought that the Indians would rather have a few captives to take home than be forced to fight in bitter winter weather.

Boone led Blackfish and the Shawnees to the Blue Licks. As they approached the

[*141*]

springs, Boone called out to his men, "You are surrounded by Indians. The Shawnees agree to treat you well if you give up."

The salt-makers were amazed. But there was nothing they could do. They gave up their rifles and surrendered. Shawnee braves hurried to make them prisoners. After the Indians had thrown away three hundred bushels of salt, the war party headed north through the snow with their prisoners.

They had hardly made camp that night when Boone saw the warriors line up in two lines with a path left between them. This was the gauntlet that the Indians usually made their captives run.

Daniel went up to Blackfish. "Chief Blackfish," he said, "I did not think you would go back on your word." He pointed to the rows of Indian men near the huts. "I asked you not to make my men run the gauntlet."

Blackfish patted him on the shoulder and grinned slyly. "I'm keeping my promise. Your men are not going through the line. But *you* are. You did not ask me to promise to keep you from the gauntlet."

It was true. Daniel had been so intent on keeping his men unhurt, he had forgotten to include himself in the promise.

Boone stood at the head of the two lines of warriors and looked down the lane between them. The other end seemed a long way off. Each warrior had a club or knife or tomahawk in his hand ready to hurt him.

"Get ready, boys," Boone called, "I'm coming a-flying."

Daniel ran. The first Indian in line swung his club at him. Daniel dodged, then cut across out of reach of the man on the other side of the line. Back and forth Boone dodged, but all the time he was making his way down the line toward the other end.

Once a club hit his shoulder. Another Shawnee managed to stab him in the wrist with a knife. But most of the blows of the tomahawks he ducked.

He was almost at the end of the line and panting hard. An Indian stepped out of line, squarely in front of Boone, in order to get a good swing at him.

The white hunter did not wait. He charged

He charged at the Indian with lowered head

at the Indian with lowered head and butted him to the ground. Then he dashed as fast as he could the rest of the way.

Boone was out of the gauntlet line. The Indians gathered around him, laughing and patting him on the back. He was their friend now, though a moment ago they had done their best to harm him.

Blackfish came up. "Indians have much fun," he said through the interpreter. "Indians like gauntlet."

Boone didn't answer. He hadn't been very badly hurt, but still he thought this was a poor idea of fun.

The next morning the Indians and their captives left camp early. After nine days of hard travel, they reached the Shawnee town of Little Chillicothe which was north of the Ohio River.

Blackfish led the white hunter to his hut, and there Daniel lived. A few months later the old chief adopted Boone as his son.

Daniel was now a Shawnee and his Indian name was Sheltowee, which meant Big Turtle. Day after day he went about the Shawnee

[*145*]

town, whistling and singing. He wanted the Indians to think he was happy as a member of their tribe. But every day he managed to hide away some lead and powder so that he would be ready if a chance came to escape.

One day Boone found several guns, which belonged to the braves, lying beside a hut. When no one was looking, he took the lead bullets from inside the gun barrels.

"Blackfish," he called to his adopted father who was standing near by, "I'm going to leave." He began to walk away.

Blackfish shouted for his warriors and they picked up their guns and fired at the white hunter. Boone turned around and pretended to catch all of the bullets shot at him.

Then he walked back and gave one lead ball to each warrior. "Sheltowee is a great magician," he said to them. "Bullets do not hurt me. But I think I'll stay with you awhile."

Blackfish laughed at his adopted son, and said, "Good trick, Sheltowee."

Spring came and Boone heard Blackfish discussing plans with other chiefs to leave for Boonesborough with a great party of warriors.

He rode off through the trees toward the south

He realized he must escape soon, if he expected to warn the fort.

A short time after that, he went with a group of red hunters to shoot turkeys. Out in the woods they found a large flock. The warriors ran at the birds, yelling and screaming. The turkeys flew up into the trees. Then the warriors slipped among the trees and shot them, one by one.

Boone waited until he heard the braves shooting. Then he walked over to where a horse was tied He jumped on the animal.

The women who were waiting to take the dead turkeys home ran toward him His adopted mother screamed, "Sheltowee, come back! Blackfish be angry if you go."

"Tell Blackfish I forgot to bring a clean shirt with me," Daniel grinned. "I aim to go home and get it. Fare thee well, Mother."

Boone rode off through the trees toward the south.

CHAPTER THIRTEEN

Shawnees Lay Siege

Boone clutched the horse with his long legs as he galloped through the trees. He could hear the cries of the Shawnee women behind him. He knew the warriors would be following him on their horses in a short time.

He reached a shallow creek and headed downstream, riding right in the middle of the water. He wanted to throw the Indians off his trail until he could get to his hidden supplies.

Rounding a bend, he rode up the bank and into the woods again. Soon he reached the hollow log where he had stored smoked deer meat, powder and lead, and a gun. He jumped down and hurriedly grabbed up the provisions. Then he remounted and was off again.

All that day and night he rode, sometimes

through the woods, sometimes on trails when he felt it was safe. By morning, however, he was still north of the Ohio River and in Shawnee territory.

Try as he would, he could not urge the horse to greater speed. The animal's sides were heaving and its hide glistened with sweat in the sun. Finally, at a creek, the horse stopped and refused to go any farther.

Boone jumped down, walked into the water and waded off downstream. He knew that if the Indians followed him this far, it would take time and trouble to find where he had left the creek and struck off through the trees.

That afternoon he reached the Ohio River. Much to his delight he found on the bank a birch bark canoe with a hole in it. He stuffed some moss and leaves in the hole and started across. By twilight he had reached the Kentucky shore.

By this time Boone had ridden and walked for almost two days without sleep and with very little food. Nevertheless, he ate the last of his jerked meat and started off at once for Boonesborough.

He had no idea how soon the Shawnees would attack the fort. But he knew there was much to be done there before the Indians came. He felt he must go on.

Two days later he went wearily across the clearing around the Boonesborough fort. It had taken him four days of hard traveling to get there.

The gates were open, but a man with a long rifle lounged near the entrance. It was his brother, Squire Boone.

Squire ran toward the thin, exhausted-looking man.

"Dan'l!" he shouted. "Is it really you? We were sure you was dead. Rebecca and the children have gone back to Caroliny."

"To Caroliny?" Boone stopped in surprise. All the long, dangerous journey home, he'd looked forward to seeing his wife and children. And now he found they were gone

"Five months is a long time, Dan'l," said Squire gently. "Jemima's here. Don't fret about Rebecca. You can fetch her back soon."

"No," answered Daniel. "She and the tads are better off where they are. The Shawnees will be after us soon, Squire, and they'll have a heap of men and a power of guns and lead."

"We'll be ready for them," Squire promised. "But you need rest and food now You can worry about the Injuns later." And he helped his brother into the fort.

In a few days Boone was as good as new. He helped the settlers strengthen the fort The old rotten logs in the stockade were replaced with strong new ones. Bullets were molded, food and water were stored inside the fort, and scouts were sent out to watch for the Shawnee war party.

"Maybe I ought to go to Caroliny," Daniel thought after all these preparations had been made. "I hate for Rebecca and the young 'uns to think I'm dead." Suddenly he slapped his leg and decided, "No, I won't go until we've whipped the Injuns. I'll stay in Boonesborough and help my friends and my kin fight. I'll just stick around and see that Blackfish gets a hot welcome of lead from his son, Sheltowee."

Then one September morning the scouts reported a Shawnee war party of over four hundred men approaching Boonesborough. Four hundred! Things looked bad for the settlers. Though several men had come from Harrodsburg and fifteen had come from Logan's Station, there was still only a small force in the fort. Boone counted thirty men, twenty boys, and a few women and children.

But the frontiersmen were determined not to surrender to the Shawnees. They might be outnumbered, but they would not give up till the walls of the fort collapsed under the attack.

Boone looked around the fort at the men waiting with their rifles at the loopholes. "Let 'em come, we're ready," he said.

[153]

Before long Blackfish and his warriors surrounded the fort. The old Shawnee chief expected Boonesborough to surrender at once. But the pioneers refused, and the fight was on.

The Indians rushed toward the fort, firing and yelling. Daniel shouted, "Let 'em have a taste of lead, boys."

He stuck his rifle through a loophole in the stockade wall. He sighted down the barrel at a Shawnee and pulled the trigger. The Indian fell.

Quickly Daniel poured powder down the barrel from his horn, took a lead ball from his shot bag and put it in the rifle. He shoved the bullet home with his ramrod. Now his gun was reloaded and ready to fire.

There was no talking as the men fired and loaded and fired again. Cows had been herded together in the open space inside the fort. They mooed in terror. A dog barked and a little boy yelled, "Shut up, Red Boy!"

Soon the Shawnees withdrew to the trees at the bottom of the slope. Here they were out of range of the guns at the fort.

The rest of that day the men stood at the

loopholes. But the Indians did not charge the fort again.

All the hot fall afternoon Jemima carried a piggin of water around to the men at the loopholes. Once her father stopped her to take a drink. "Thank ye, Jemima," he said as he handed the dipper back. "Is anybody bad hurt?"

"No, Pa," she answered.

"Good. We'll need every man tonight," Boone commented. "No telling what that rascal Blackfish will try to do next."

The night settled down, black and still. Boone knew the Indians were up to something. They were *too* quiet. He listened hard as he stared out into the darkness. Once he thought he saw a shadow near the fort, but he wasn't certain.

Then there was an unexpected bright glare. A man from the blockhouse yelled to the others, "They're setting the fence on fire!"

The old rail fence which ran up the slope right to the very walls of the fort had been set on fire. The Indians had piled dried brush and flax along the fence, so it would burn better.

[155]

All afternoon Jemima carried water to the men

The flames leaped high, burning rapidly toward them. If the fire reached the walls of the fort, Boonesborough was lost.

"Squire, you and Stafford bring shovels over here," yelled Boone. "We'll tunnel under the fort walls and put out that fire."

Men ran up with shovels and began to dig at the bottom of the upright logs. Soon they had a trench under the wooden wall and out to the fence. It was big enough so that several men could get in it at the same time. Yet they would be hidden from the Indians.

"Tear down the fence," Daniel ordered. He climbed into the trench with his brother and a few others. When they had crawled under the wall and were outside the fort, they crouched in the trench while they pulled the burning rails away from the wooden walls.

Boonesborough was saved for the time being and not a man was hurt. Boone crawled back inside the fort, wondering what the Shawnees would think of next.

The following day the settlers in the stockade heard the sound of axes in the woods. Boone went to the second story of the blockhouse to look out

[157]

"Dan'l, what are them red devils up to?" asked one of the settlers.

Boone grinned. "They're cutting down trees for exercise. We didn't give them much of a fight yesterday."

"They outrun every bullet I shot at 'em," the man laughed. "I'd think they'd be plumb wore out."

Boone looked out toward the river. The Indians were working along the steep riverbank, out of sight of the fort. All at once the sound of axes stopped.

Boone saw that something was wrong with the Kentucky River. He looked upstream. Clear and green there. But down the river the water was yellow with mud.

"Boys, the Shawnees are digging a tunnel under our fort," Boone announced and he rubbed his whiskers. "There's only one thing to do and that's dig a tunnel from inside and meet them underground."

The men got shovels and started to dig.

Day after day, work continued in both tunnels. There was no fighting at all. Occasionally one of the settlers took a pot shot at the enemy.

[*158*]

Most of the time, however, the Shawnees stayed out of sight.

The tunnels came closer to each other. The Boonesborough men could hear the soft thumps in the earth as the Indians dug steadily closer to them. The settlers grew tense and nervous with waiting. Nobody slept much. Water was getting scarce. The cattle bawled constantly from thirst and fear.

Boone kept constant watch. He joked with the men and told the women not to worry. But all the time he kept telling himself, "Something's got to happen soon. We can't hold out much longer."

Then on the seventh night of the siege, something did happen.

It was dark. A few stars were out, but starlight is no light for shooting. In the fort even the cattle had ceased bellowing. A whippoorwill called from down the river.

At that moment a fiery arrow came from the cliff across the river. It arched high in the air and landed on a cabin roof. Another and then another flaming arrow followed the first. The night was bright with the light.

[159]

Then up the slope toward the fort dashed Indians with lighted torches. Close to the fort the red men stopped, and flung the burning torches over the fort walls. One fell among the horses and they stampeded, dashing about inside the fort in fright. The men shouted in alarm. The women screamed, the children cried, the cows took up their pitiful bawling.

"Some of you get on the roof and beat those fires out," Boone called. "Don't all go. The rest stay at the loopholes and shoot the Injuns bringing up more torches."

[160]

Some of the men climbed to the roofs and beat out the fires with wet deerskins. The burning arrows rained down out of the dark sky.

More and more men worked to put out the fires. Some of the women took their places at the loopholes and fired rifles at the Indians.

The Indian torches had set the stockade afire at several places. It seemed as though Boonesborough was lost.

"The water's getting low," the settlers told each other grimly. They knew that when the water went, they would just have to let the place burn.

Suddenly it began to rain. Just a slow drizzle at first, but it fell harder as the night went by. The fires were put out. The log cabins and fort walls became too wet for further fires to catch.

The Indians gave up shooting their fiery arrows. The night was quiet. The cattle drank the rain water and hushed their bellowing. There was no sound but the falling rain on the cabin roofs. Boonesborough was saved once more.

[*161*]

Early the next morning Boone was up scanning the wet woods for sign of the Indians. The rain had stopped, but it was still cloudy.

"What will they try today? Will they keep on with their tunnel?" he wondered. Then he realized he heard no sound of digging. He sent out scouts and they returned shortly to report.

"The Indians are gone! Their tunnel has caved in."

"We gave the Shawnees the licking they deserved," Squire said.

Boone looked around at the happy faces of the women and children, and he suddenly felt he could wait no longer. He had to get to Carolina and see his family.

CHAPTER FOURTEEN

Howdy Do to Missouri

A FEW weeks later Daniel Morgan Boone was at the spring, getting water for his mother. He looked up to see a tall thin man in dusty buckskins coming through the trees. There was something about that long easy walk that made Daniel Morgan drop his piggin.

"Pa! Oh, Pa!" he shouted as he ran and threw himself in his father's arms. "We thought the Injuns had you for sure."

"I thought so too," Boone replied.

Soon Daniel was seated on a stool by the fire, telling his wife and Israel and Daniel Morgan and little Rebecca and Jesse all about his capture by Blackfish, about how he escaped, and about the siege of Boonesborough.

"And you whipped the Injuns good and proper, Pa?" asked Daniel Morgan.

"Why, I turned old Blackfish across my knee and spanked him something fierce " laughed Daniel.

"Did he cry, Pa?" asked little Jesse.

"He cried so hard he put the fires out on the Boonesborough cabin roofs, Jesse," Boone answered. And they all laughed.

"Are you going back to Kentuck, Dan'l?" Mrs. Boone asked.

"I couldn't ever leave Kentuck, Rebecca,"

replied her husband. "Even the Injuns can't drive me away. You want to come back, don't ye?"

"Yes, yes," cried the children.

Rebecca Boone smiled and answered, "I don't aim to be left behind."

Daniel Boone took his family back to the meadowlands of Kentucky. More and more people settled in Kentucky. The British sent the Indians time and again against the white settlers there. And the pioneers did not always win. At the Battle of Blue Licks in 1782, the Kentuckians lost the battle and some of their best fighters as well.

It was a sad time for everybody. Boone saw his oldest son, Israel, killed before his eyes. But Daniel and Rebecca and the other families would not leave Kentucky.

The British were defeated and the Revolutionary War came to an end in 1782. The thirteen American colonies gained their independence and became the thirteen United States.

The pioneers in Kentucky felt that they had helped to win the war. They had not fought any British armies, but they had fought the Indians day after day. They had done their part in creating the United States of America. And ten years after the war's end, Kentucky was admitted to the Union as the fifteenth state.

Times were easier now, but game was scarce. Deer and buffalo and bear didn't stay long in a country where people lived. The forests were cut down to make fields, roads were built for wagons to drive over, and the animals left.

But Daniel Boone still liked to hunt. One day he called his wife out of the cabin beside the Big Sandy River where they now lived.

"Rebecca, I got something I want you to see," he said.

Mrs. Boone came slowly out of the cabin and made her way toward her husband. "What is it, Dan'l?"

Daniel placed his hand on a big tulip poplar tree. "See this here tree?"

Mrs. Boone nodded. She had seen hundreds of those big trees in her day. They were pretty trees in the spring with their orange and green flowers. "Looks just like any other tulip tree," she told Daniel.

[166]

"Well, it ain't," he answered. "I'm a-fixing to cut this tree down and make me a dugout. Then I'm aiming to float down the Ohio River across the Mississippi River to the country of Missouri."

Rebecca turned startled eyes to her husband. "Make a boat and move at your age? Dan'l, I declare, I believe you're touched in the head." She paused and added, "Besides that's Spanish territory in Missouri. I heard Daniel Morgan say so."

"Well, it may be Spanish land, but the deer don't know it," remarked Daniel. "I hear that deer is so thick in the Missouri country, you can walk on their backs from one salt lick to another."

Rebecca laughed. "Sounds like Kentuck in the days when we were first married. You used to talk just that way. And have that same faraway look in your eye." She sighed. "I reckon I might as well not argue with you. You're after more elbow room as always. I'll go with you, Dan'l."

Soon, all over Kentucky, folks were saying that Daniel Boone was leaving for Missouri.

Some people decided to go along with him.

"We'll go where Daniel goes," they said. "He'll take us where the game's plentiful and the land's good. And he'll stick with us through any kind of danger or hardship."

Most of the pioneers decided to travel in dugout canoes, which would float down the Ohio River. Rebecca Boone planned to go in Daniel's big dugout with two of her sons, Nathan and Daniel Morgan, and her daughter, Jemima Boone Callaway. Squire Boone would journey down the river too.

But Daniel Boone decided he could trust no one but himself to see that the cows and the pack horses got safely to Missouri.

"I'd rather walk any day than have to sit still in a boat," the hunter told Flanders Callaway, who was going to walk with him. He winked at his son-in-law and added, "Besides we can do a little hunting on the way."

One September day in 1799, neighbors and friends of the Boones gathered around the log cabin on the banks of the Big Sandy River. It was a warm morning and sunlight sparkled on the water. Men sat on stumps in the clearing around the cabin, and women stood in the

shade of maples which were already beginning
to turn red and orange. A redwing blackbird
called from the tall purple blooming iron-
weed, "Konk-la-reeee!"

Then Boone came out of the cabin, carrying
a bundle of quilts on his shoulder. The crowd
began to call out to him as he made his way toward them.

"Don't forget to put out the fire in the
cabin, Dan'l."

"Call up the cow, Dan'l is ready to go to
Missouri," another joked.

Boone smiled at them and made his way
down the riverbank to the large dugout which
was tied to a tree. He placed the quilts in the
bottom of the boat. Scattered at intervals in
the forty-foot dugout were wooden chests,
bundles of clothes, seed corn in leather bags,
a cask of powder, and several iron pots.

Mrs. Boone and Jemima came down the
bank, followed by the two boys. Daniel helped
his wife and daughter into the boat. When the
two young men were seated and had picked up
their paddles, Boone untied the dugout and
pushed it out into the current

Squire Boone and his family were in a

smaller dugout, and a neighbor traveled in a third. The three boats moved slowly off downstream. As they floated down to the Ohio, they would meet the other settlers who were going to Missouri.

"You Boone folks come back to see us sometime," a woman called out across the water. Everybody waved and called good-by.

Rebecca Boone turned and waved to her husband. Then the boats passed out of sight around a bend.

[170]

Daniel made his way to where Jemima's husband, Flanders Callaway, waited with some other men who wanted to move to Missouri. A long string of pack horses stood quietly swishing their tails at the flies. A cow strayed from the herd and had to be driven back.

"You folks ready?" Daniel asked. The men all nodded. Flanders handed Boone his long rifle. Daniel took it and turned to the crowd standing near by. "Don't you folks eat any green persimmons," he said. "And if'n you git to Missouri, come set a spell with me."

He moved off westward, leading the horses. As the group crossed Kentucky, people who knew they were coming gathered along the way to see this great old woodsman. At almost every town, friends gathered to bid him good-by, friends who had fought through the siege of Boonesborough and the bloody years of the Indian wars. Newcomers to Kentucky were there beside the roadway too, curious to see Daniel Boone, the man who had done so much to win this rich land.

At Harrodsburg one man stood among the

[*171*]

crowd waiting for the Boone party to come through the town. He had his thumbs stuck cockily in the pockets of his fancy vest. Turning to his neighbor, he asked, "Say, did you ever see this fellow, Boone?"

The other shook his head. "I just come to Kentucky last month, but I've heard a lot about him. Why, I hear Boone has killed every deer he's ever shot at in his life."

"I wonder if it's so. I heard he could smell out an Indian trail like a bloodhound," the other remarked. "There's some wild tales about him, all right."

Someone in the crowd called out, "Here he comes. Here comes Boone."

A tall, straight man in homespuns came toward the group. His white hair was long and clubbed in back. He wore an old black brimmed hat. Over his shoulder he carried a flintlock rifle. He was at the head of a line of pack horses. Other men were with him driving the cows at the rear of the horses.

"Yea, Dan'l! Don't let the Injuns get you in Missouri," someone shouted.

Daniel glanced at the crowd. He didn't like

[172]

"It ain't never good-by. It's howdy do."

crowds around hollering at a fellow. "Bad as the yelling Shawnee Injuns," he said to himself. "And there ain't a one of them newcomers with their fancy clothes who can tell a buffalo from a blade of grass. Humph!"

"Fare thee well, Daniel Boone," an old woman called out in a high voice. "Don't forget us folks in Kentuck, for we'll never forget you!"

"Kill a deer for me, Dan'l," shouted another oldtimer.

Daniel's bright blue eyes swept over the crowd as he approached them, and then to the trees beyond the town. He had fought for this land. He had lost two sons trying to settle it. He was sad for a moment.

Then he thought, "There's deer and bear waiting for me to shoot in Missouri. And there's rich land waiting for me. There's even Injuns out there, craving for a fight."

Daniel made his way slowly through the crowd, nodding solemnly to them. He had never liked to talk to a crowd of folks, only a few of whose faces he recognized. At last he was clear of the noisy group and walking past the last house in the town.

"Good-by, Dan'l," came the final call.

Daniel stopped and waved to the people. Then he turned to Flanders Callaway and remarked, "As long as there are deer to shoot and I can draw a rifle bead on them, it ain't never good-by. It's howdy do."

He pulled on the line tied to the pack horses and moved on west again.

About the Author

WILLIAM O. STEELE was born in Franklin, Tennessee, where, as a boy, he hunted the fresh-plowed fields for arrowheads. He graduated from college in 1940 and spent the next five years in the army. In 1943 he married but was not discharged from the army until his oldest child was nearly a year old. As she grew older, he read to her and this led to his interest in children's books. He began to write stories of pioneer days for boys and girls. He now has three children and lives on Lookout Mountain, among the same kinds of hills and trees Dan'l Boone saw. He likes to talk to mountaineers and Cherokee Indians, our strongest link with the pioneer past.

About the Artist

WARREN BAUMGARTNER, who was born in Oakville, Missouri, has been an enthusiastic hunter and fisherman ever since he was a boy. He has always loved the outdoors, and even as a youngster made a hobby of sketching the different birds and animals he saw in the woods. When he finished school, he had already decided to become an artist. He studied at Washington University Art School, the Chicago Art Institute, and the Grand Central Art School in New York. Soon his work was being exhibited all over the country. His watercolors have won several awards, the latest being the Chauncey F. Ryder Purchase Prize at the American Watercolor Exhibit.

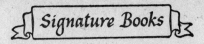

Signature Books

"Names That Made History"

ENID LaMONTE MEADOWCROFT, *Supervising Editor*